Eternal Pursuit

The Mormon Trivia Book

Eternal Pursuit

The Mormon Trivia Book

Jay A. Parry

Bookcraft

Salt Lake City, Utah

Library of Congress Catalog Card Number: 85-73001
ISBN 0-88494-578-2

First Printing, 1985

Printed in the United States of America

Eternal Pursuit: The Mormon Trivia Book was created by Jay A. Parry. Assisting in writing the questions were the following:

Lane Johnson

Gary B. Keeley

R. Stephen Marshall

Bonnie McIntyre

Larry E. Morris

Eric C. Olson

Donald W. Parry

Jay A. Parry

Michael D. Parry

Kevin Talbot

Key to Abbreviations
in the Answers

ABM   *A Book of Mormons*, Richard Van Wagoner and Steven Walker

BD   Bible Dictionary, LDS edition of the King James Version of the Bible

BG   *Bible Gazetteer*, LDS edition of the King James Version of the Bible

BP   *A Believing People*, Richard Cracroft and Neal Lambert

BYU   *BYU Today*

CA   *Deseret News Church Almanac*

CHC   *A Comprehensive History of The Church of Jesus Christ of Latter-day Saints*, B. H. Roberts

CN   *Church News*

CS   *A Century of Singing*, J. Spencer Cornwall

D   *Dialogue: A Journal of Mormon Thought*

DCOMS   *The Doctrine and Covenants, Our Modern Scripture*, Richard O. Cowan

DN   *Deseret News*

ECH   *Essentials in Church History*, Joseph Fielding Smith

EN   *Ensign*

ES   *Exceptional Stories from the Lives of Our Prophets*, Leon Hartshorn, compiler

ETN   *Ensign to the Nations*, Russell Rich

GMBYUS   *Greatest Moments in BYU Sports*, Brad Rock and Lee Warnick

HC   *History of The Church of Jesus Christ of Latter-day Saints*, Joseph Smith

HH   *Horizontal Harmony of the Four Gospels in Parallel Columns*, Thomas M. Mumford

Hymns	*Hymns*, The Church of Jesus Christ of Latter-day Saints (1948)
JSR	*Joseph Smith and the Restoration*, Ivan J. Barrett
MA	*Mormon Athletes*, William Black
MA II	*Mormon Athletes II*, William Black
MD	*Mormon Doctrine*, Bruce R. McConkie
ME	*The Mormon Experience: A History of the Latter-day Saints*, Leonard J. Arrington and Davis Bitton
MGI	*The Mormon Graphic Image, 1834–1914*, Gary L. Bunker and Davis Bitton
MMZ	*Mighty Men of Zion: General Authorities of the Last Dispensation*, Lawrence R. Flake
NE	*New Era*
NS	*A Noble Son, Spencer W. Kimball*, Institute of Family Research
NTT	*Nibley on the Timely and the Timeless*, Hugh Nibley
OHUM	*Outline History of Utah and the Mormons*, Gustive O. Larsen
OSGA	*Outstanding Stories by General Authorities*, Leon Hartshorn, compiler
RS	*Remarkable Stories from the Lives of Latter-day Saint Women*, Leon Hartshorn, compiler
SBD	*Smith's Bible Dictionary*, William Smith
SEC	*Strong's Exhaustive Concordance of the Bible*, James Strong
SMH	*Stories of Our Mormon Hymns*, J. Spencer Cornwall
SOOC	*The Story of Our Church for Young Latter-day Saints*, Emma Marr Petersen
SWK	*Spencer W. Kimball*, Edward Kimball and Andrew Kimball
SWM	*Sing with Me: Songs for Children*
TP	*This People*
TPJS	*Teachings of the Prophet Joseph Smith*, Joseph Fielding Smith, compiler
WW	*Win If You Will*, Paul H. Dunn

Contents

How to Use This Book

Eternal Pursuit is a book of "trivia," but it is also much more than that. It contains some of the most important information in the world, much of it hardly trivia from an eternal perspective.

The book is divided into six parts: Old Testament, New Testament, Book of Mormon, Church History, People, and Arts and Entertainment. Besides the regular level of question difficulty, each part contains fifty simpler questions for use as needed. These are the last fifty questions in each part.

Flip to any section of the book and you can readily see how it is arranged. The questions are printed on each left-hand page, the answers being shown opposite them on the facing right-hand page. Each set of questions and answers is numbered, with the number of each question matching the number of the corresponding answer.

There are several fun ways to use this book:

• Read it on your own, Cover the right-hand page with a piece of paper while you answer the questions to yourself—perhaps jotting the answers down on the paper—then uncover the answer page to see how you did.

• Use it as a game book with family and friends. Take turns asking questions and giving answers. Choose categories at random, in sequence, or in any order you wish. You may decide to do all the questions on one page before moving on, or you may roll some dice to determine the number of the question you are to answer. Keep score by simply marking down how many questions each person answered correctly. The player with the highest number wins.

• Use it as a source of supplementary questions for any of the popular trivia board games on the national and LDS markets.

• Use it as a teaching tool. Strengthen your knowledge of the gospel, and that of your children, while having fun at the same time.

• Play it in the car while making either short or long trips. The book will cut down on boredom and enhance the journey for the entire family.

In whatever way you choose to use *Eternal Pursuit: The Mormon Trivia Book*, it will provide you with many hours of rich enjoyment. And much of what you learn from it will not be trivial at all!

PART **1** Old Testament

1. Who was Noah's father?

2. What whole nation was smitten with a plague while they were eating quail?

3. What prophet married the daughter of an Egyptian priest?

4. How was Israel cleansed of murders by unknown persons?

5. Ecclesiastes says there is "a time to kill, and a time to" what?

6. Who was the father of King Solomon?

7. What kingdom did Esarhaddon, Sargon, and Shalmanesar all reign over?

8. In what room of the temple did the ark of the covenant sit?

9. Abner was the captain of what king's army?

10. When were the Israelites commanded to eat bitter herbs?

11. Who was the last-born son of Jacob and Rachel?

12. Isaiah said, "Though your sins be as scarlet, they shall be as white as" what?

13. Which of Joseph's brothers saved him from being murdered by the other brothers?

14. Who was the father of Dinah?

15. What Old Testament name is the Hebrew form of Jesus?

16. When was a woman considered unclean for seven to fourteen days?

17. What Bible hero slew both a lion and a bear?

18. Who appeared to Moses at the site of the burning bush?

19. When Nebuchadnezzar and his army looted the Jerusalem temple, where did they take the temple vessels and treasures?

20. What words were engraved upon the sacred hat of the Levite high priest?

21. What prophet prayed to die?

22. Was Sarah alive when her grandson Jacob was born?

23. What did Jacob give to Esau in trade for the birthright?

24. When Moses learned about the golden calf, what did he do with the stone tablets?

25. By what name was Jedidiah more commonly known?

26. What prophet, besides Joel, says that in the last days the Lord's house will be established in the top of the mountains?

27. Why was Esau called Edom?

1. Lamech (Gen. 5:28−29)

2. The Israelites (Num. 11:32−33)

3. Joseph (Gen. 41:45)

4. By the performance of ritual acts, including beheading a heifer (Deut. 21:1−9)

5. A time to heal (Eccl. 3:3)

6. King David (2 Sam. 12:24)

7. Assyria (*SBD*, p. 179)

8. The holy of holies (*SBD*, p. 49)

9. Saul's (2 Sam. 2:8)

10. At the passover meal (Exod. 12:8)

11. Benjamin (Gen. 35:18)

12. Snow (Isa. 1:18)

13. Reuben (Gen 37:21)

14. Jacob (Gen. 30:21)

15. Joshua (*SBD*, p. 287)

16. After she had given birth (Lev. 12:2−5)

17. David (1 Sam. 14:5−6)

18. The Lord (Exod. 3:2)

19. To Babylon (2 Chron. 36:18)

20. "Holiness to the Lord" (*SBD*, p. 238)

21. Elijah (1 Kings 19:4)

22. No, she died soon after the marriage of Isaac and Rebekah (Gen. 24:67)

23. Bread and pottage of lentils (Gen. 25:34)

24. He cast them down and broke them (Exod 32:19)

25. Solomon (2 Sam. 12:24−25)

26. Isaiah (Isa. 2:2−4)

27. Because he sold his birth-right for Edom (red) pottage (Gen. 25:30)

28. Who was the most famous son of Jesse?

29. What group of men wore a breastplate, ephod, robe, coat, mitre, and girdle?

30. What prophet went up in a whirlwind into heaven?

31. What Benjamite king inquired of the witch of Endor for revelation?

32. How many Old Testament men were named Dodo?

33. Why did Absalom, son of David, kill his brother Amnon?

34. What was the Mosiac penalty for following after spiritualism (familiar spirits, wizards, divinations)?

35. What did Joseph Smith say about the Song of Solomon?

36. What Hebrew prophet married an Ethiopian?

37. What Israelite king imported apes?

38. What was the Mosaic penalty for those who worked on the Sabbath day?

39. Which tribe did Aaron belong to?

40. What were the Israelite "cities of refuge" used for?

41. Who said that in the last days there would be a famine, not of food or drink, "but of hearing the words of the Lord"?

42. During the days of what Israelite leader did the sun and the moon stand still?

43. The preacher of Ecclesiates says the day of death is is better than what?

44. In what two languages was the Old Testament originally written?

45. What was the capital of Israel's southern kingdom?

46. Why was King Jehoiakim murdered, his body dragged, and then buried with an ass outside the gates of Jerusalem?

47. What was dung used for during Old Testament times besides fertilizer?

48. What seasoning was to be used with every sacrificial offering?

49. What group of men, women, and children were cast into a den of lions?

50. Was Huldah a prophetess, harlot, queen, or prophet's mother?

51. How many years did Jacob work for Laban?

52. What was the Mosaic penalty for being a wizard?

53. What period of time was Isaiah speaking of when he prophesied that the "lion shall eat straw like an ox"?

54. What was Jerusalem called during the reign of King David?

28. David (1 Sam. 17:12)

29. The Levite priests (Exod. 28:4)

30. Elijah (2 Kings 2:11)

31. Saul (1 Sam. 28:6—7)

32. Three (Judg. 10:1; 2 Sam. 23:9, 24)

33. Because Amnon violated their sister, Tamar (2 Sam. 13)

34. Excommunication (Lev. 20:6)

35. It is not inspired scripture

36. Moses (Num. 12:1)

37. Solomon (1 Kings 10:22)

38. They were put to death (Exod. 31:15)

39. Levi (Exod. 4:14)

40. Temporary places of refuge for those who committed involuntary homicide (Num. 35:6—15)

41. Amos (Amos 8:11)

42. Joshua (Josh. 10:12—13)

43. "The day of one's birth" (Eccl. 7:1)

44. Hebrew and Aramaic

45. Jerusalem (*SBD*, p. 315)

46. Because he was evil in the sight of Jehovah (*SBD*, p. 271)

47. Fuel (*SBD*, p. 152)

48. Salt (Lev. 2:13)

49. The false accusers of Daniel (Dan. 6:24)

50. Prophetess (2 Kings 22:14)

51. Twenty — seven for Rachel, seven for Leah, and six for the cattle (Gen. 31:41)

52. Death (Lev. 20:27)

53. The Millennium (Isa. 11:7)

54. Jerusalem (2 Sam. 5:7, 9)

55. What patriarch's name means "father of a multitude"?

56. What Old Testament book is read during the Jewish festival of Purim commemorating the victory of Mordecai over Haman?

57. After the Lord slew Nabal the fool, what well-known Jew did Nabal's wife Abigail marry?

58. In what city were found Mount Moriah, Mount Zion, and the Mount of Olives?

59. Where did the name *Samaria* come from?

60. The firstling males of the flock and herd were used for what purpose?

61. Who gave the Israelites five golden mice?

62. Who talked with an ass?

63. What happened to Jeroboam's hand when he stretched it out to arrest a prophet?

64. What happened to the forty-two children who mocked a prophet?

65. What kind of oil was used for anointing the Levite priests?

66. What item of Goliath's did David take after he slew him?

67. Why did the Lord cause David and Bathsheba's firstborn son to die?

68. Describe a typical Old Testament Palestinian house.

69. Why did Nehemiah and the Jews have to arm themselves while rebuilding the walls of Jerusalem?

70. Who caught three hundred foxes and burned their tails?

71. Joseph had his silver cup hidden in the belongings of which of his brothers?

72. Who was the firstborn son of Jacob and Leah?

73. How did Joseph become the second greatest ruler of Egypt?

74. On what day of the year was the high priest permitted to enter the Holy of Holies of the temple?

75. After David was anointed king of Israel, what city became his capital?

76. Exodus says that "the cloud of the Lord was upon the tabernacle by day." What was on it by night?

77. What food were the Israelites allowed to sell to strangers but not permitted to eat themselves?

78. Ishbosheth, successor to King Saul for two years, was the son of what king?

79. What prophet was the son of the prophet Iddo and a contemporary of the prophet Haggai?

55. Abraham's (Gen. 17:5−6)

56. Esther (*SBD*, p. 557)

57. David (1 Sam. 25:38−42)

58. Jerusalem (*SBD*, p. 283)

59. It was named after the man who originally owned the land (1 Kings 16:24)

60. As sacrifices to the Lord (Deut. 15:19−22)

61. The Philistines (1 Sam. 6:4−5)

62. Balaam (Num. 22:28−30)

63. It withered and was paralyzed (1 Kings 13:1−5)

64. Two she-bears tore them up (2 Kings 2:23−24)

65. Olive oil (Exod. 30:24)

66. His sword (1 Sam. 21:9)

67. Because of their adulterous act (2 Sam. 12:11 − 18)

68. One room, one story, with a flat roof, and made of stone (*SBD*, p. 246)

69. Because their enemies threatened to hinder their work (Neh. 4)

70. Samson (Judg. 15:4−5)

71. Benjamin (Gen. 44:2)

72. Reuben (Gen. 29:32)

73. He found favor with the Pharaoh by interpreting his dream (Gen. 41)

74. The Day of Atonement (*SBD*, p. 61)

75. Jerusalem (2 Sam. 5)

76. Fire (Exod. 40:38)

77. That which died of itself (Deut. 14:21)

78. Saul (2 Sam. 2:10)

79. Zechariah (*SBD*, p. 758)

80. Why did Joab, captain of David's army, murder Abner, captain of Saul's army?

81. Who dipped their brother's coat in goat kid's blood?

82. In what century did King Zedekiah of Jerusalem, King Nebuchadnezzar, and King Cyrus of Persia reign?

83. What woman was a prophetess and judge of Israel?

84. Where did the Israelites dwell while in Egypt?

85. The walls of what city were so thick that homes were built upon them?

86. What was the Mosaic penalty for eating blood?

87. Ecclesiastes says that "there is no new thing under" what?

88. Who was the firstborn son of Joseph and Asenath?

89. What unique material was Ahab's house made of?

90. What ancient city had no less than twenty-two gates in its protecting walls?

91. Who said, "Whither thou goest, I will go; and where thou lodgest, I will lodge"?

92. Alexandria, a noted city of Egypt, was founded by whom?

93. What was a person called who consecrated himself by abstaining from strong drink and by never cutting his hair?

94. When were *two* golden calves worshipped by the Israelites?

95. What heavy man (who was a high priest and a judge) fell off a seat and broke his neck?

96. What son of Abraham inherited all that Abraham owned?

97. What people built David's palace and Solomon's temple?

98. Which of Bathsheba's husbands had a name that means "Jehovah is my light"?

99. Under the law of Moses, how often each week were sacrifices to be offered?

100. Why did Jacob send his ten sons to Egypt?

101. Who was Zipporah married to?

102. Besides being a prophet, what other responsibility did Samuel have concerning the Israelites?

103. What did the three prophets Nathan, Ahijah, and Iddo have in common?

104. What prophet (who was also a judge) killed the Amalekite King Agag with a sword?

80. Because Abner had killed Joab's brother (2 Sam. 2–3)

81. The brothers of Joseph (Gen. 37:31–33)

82. Sixth century B.C. (2 Chron. 36)

83. Deborah (Judg. 4:4–5)

84. The land of Goshen (Gen. 45:10)

85. Jericho (Josh. 2:15)

86. Excommunication (Lev. 7:26–27)

87. The sun (Eccl. 1:9)

88. Manasseh (Gen. 41:51)

89. Ivory (1 Kings 22:39)

90. Jerusalem (SBD, p. 283)

91. Ruth (Ruth 1:16)

92. Alexander the Great (SBD, p. 31)

93. A Nazarite (Num. 6:1–5)

94. During the days of Jeroboam (1 Kings 12:28–33)

95. Eli (1 Sam. 4:15, 18)

96. Isaac (Gen. 25:5)

97. The Phoenicians (SBD, p. 241)

98. Uriah (2 Sam. 11:3)

99. Seven days a week (Num. 28:1–10)

100. To buy grain (Gen. 42:1–2)

101. Moses (Exod. 2:21)

102. He was judge over all Israel (11 Sam. 3:20; 7:15)

103. They all wrote "acts of Solomon" that are not found in the scriptures (2 Chron. 9:29)

104. Samuel (1 Sam. 15:32–33)

105. Who prophesied that a lion would someday eat straw?

106. Among the Israelites, what child received a double portion of the father's inheritance?

107. What did Hebrews do with their hair during times of grief or affliction?

108. Of the five "cities of the plain," which two are the most famous?

109. How many proverbs are attributed to Solomon?

110. How often did Aaron burn incense upon the altar of incense?

111. How much was Joseph sold to the Ishmeelites for?

112. Were Ebal and Gerizim Varmy the names of generals, wild animals, countries, or mountains?

113. What is the Old Testament name for the Dead Sea?

114. How were the Amorites destroyed?

115. When the Israelites encamped, where did they place the tabernacle?

116. Zimran, Jokshan, Medan, Midian, Ishbak, and Shuah were the sons of what patriarch?

117. Were the hart, gazelle, deer, and wild ox clean or unclean animals to the Israelites?

118. Was Antioch in Israel, Persia, Syria, or Arabia?

119. What city's inhabitants were totally destroyed (with the exception of Rahab and her family)?

120. How many were killed when Aphek's city wall fell?

121. What was the name of Ishmael's mother?

122. What queen was trampled underfoot by horses?

123. What beautiful damsel watered Isaac's camels and later became his wife?

124. Who wore a garment of goatskins in order to appear as his hairy brother?

125. Who was allowed to become a Nazarite—a man or a woman or both?

126. How many times are the Ten Commandments listed in the Old Testament?

127. What does the word *Hosanna*, chanted during the Feast of Tabernacles, mean?

128. What notable thing occurred during the days of Peleg?

129. Who was Jacob's second wife?

130. What country were Manasseh and Ephraim born in?

131. Who lamented over the death of Saul and Jonathan with a song?

105. Isaiah (Isa. 65:25)

106. The firstborn son (Deut. 21:17)

107. It was torn or cut off (*SBD*, p. 219)

108. Sodom and Gomorrah (*SBD*, p. 214)

109. Three thousand (1 Kings 4:32)

110. Once every morning and evening (Exod. 30:7−8)

111. Twenty pieces of silver (Gen. 37:28)

112. Mountains (Josh. 8:33)

113. Salt Sea (*SBD*, p. 139)

114. The Lord cast great stones from heaven upon them (Josh. 10:11)

115. In the center of camp (Num. 2:1)

116. Abraham (Gen. 25:1−2)

117. Clean (Deut. 14:4−5)

118. Syria (*SBD*, p. 39)

119. Jericho (Josh. 6:21−23)

120. 27,000 men (1 Kings 20:30)

121. Hagar (Gen. 16:8−11)

122. Jezebel (2 Kings 9:30)

123. Rebekah (Gen. 24)

124. Jacob (Gen. 27:15−16)

125. Both (Num. 6:2)

126. Twice (Exod. 20; Deut. 5)

127. "Save, we pray" (*SBD*, p. 244)

128. The earth was divided (Gen. 10:25)

129. Rachel (Gen. 29:28)

130. Egypt (Gen. 41:46−52)

131. David (2 Sam. 1:17−27)

132. What woman's name means "daughter of the covenant"?

133. Who successfully disguised himself from his own brothers?

134. What was the Mosaic penalty for sacrificing to false gods?

135. Within six inches, how tall was the giant Goliath?

136. Within ten, how many of the Psalms are attributed to David?

137. What was the Mosaic penalty for working on the Sabbath?

138. Who killed Saul?

139. Who caused the sun to stand still by saying, "Sun stand thou still upon Gibeon"?

140. What did God use to guard the tree of life after Adam and Eve were expelled from the garden?

141. Although Jacob was embalmed in Egypt, where did Joseph take his body to be buried?

142. What giant from Gath was slain by one of the sons of Jesse?

143. What is another name for the first book of Samuel?

144. Why was Uzzah killed by the Lord?

145. Adino the Eznite, who slew eight hundred men in battle with his spear, was a captain of whose army?

146. Within five years, how old was David when he was anointed king over the land of Judah?

147. Why did Simeon and Levi slay Shechem and all the males of his city?

148. To whom did Samuel say, "To obey is better than sacrifice"?

149. What book title is a Greek word for *origin* or *beginning*?

150. What kingdom destroyed the northern kingdom of Israel?

151. Why did David deliver up seven sons of Saul to the Gibeonites to be hanged?

152. Who was the husband of Rachel, Leah, Bilhah, and Zilpah?

153. Precisely what name did Isaiah use for the "son of the morning" who fell from heaven?

154. Who was the son of Nun?

155. Who was the father of Levi?

156. Who labored seven years so he could marry a girl, and then was tricked into marrying the girl's sister?

157. What is the first of the Ten Commandments?

132. Bathsheba (2 Sam. 11:3, footnote)

133. Joseph (Gen. 42:7−8)

134. The guilty person was killed (Exod. 22:20)

135. 10½ feet (*SBD*, p. 214)

136. Seventy-three (*SBD*, p. 550)

137. Death (Exod. 31:14)

138. He committed suicide (1 Sam. 31:4−6)

139. Joshua (Josh. 10:12−13)

140. Cherubim (Gen. 3:24)

141. To the land of Canaan (Gen. 50:1−6)

142. Goliath (1 Sam. 17)

143. The first book of the Kings (1 Samuel, subhead)

144. Because he steadied the ark of the covenant without authorization (2 Sam. 6:6−7)

145. David's (2 Sam. 23:8)

146. Thirty years old (2 Sam. 5:4)

147. Because Shechem defiled their sister Dinah (Gen. 34)

148. Saul (1 Sam. 15:22)

149. Genesis

150. Assyria (*SBD*, p. 260)

151. Because Saul had smitten the Gibeonites against the will of the Lord (2 Sam. 21:1−10)

152. Jacob (Gen. 29−30)

153. Lucifer (Isa. 14:12)

154. Joshua (1 Chron. 7:27)

155. Jacob (Gen. 29:34)

156. Jacob (Gen. 29:21−25)

157. Thou shalt have no other gods before me" (Exod. 20:3)

158. What miracle did Elisha perform with an iron axe-head?

159. Which of Jacob's wives bore his first four sons?

160. Where did Joash, who became the seven-year-old king of Judah, live the first six years of his life?

161. What was David's greatest sin?

162. What happened to Jezebel's body after her death?

163. What town was called "a city of palms"?

164. Why did Potiphar put Joseph into prison?

165. What king destroyed the wicked King Ahab and be-headed Ahab's seventy sons?

166. Why did Aaron's rod bring forth buds, blossoms, and almonds?

167. What Egyptian man had a dream of seven years of plenty and seven years of famine?

168. Within five feet, what was the wingspan and height of each cherub of Solomon's temple?

169. How many decks did Noah's ark have?

170. Who was the oldest man of the Old Testament?

171. What king pretended to worship Baal at the temple of Samaria in order to destroy all of the idolaters?

172. Who said "My God hath sent his angel, and hath shut the lions' mouths that they have not hurt me"?

173. Why did Moses command the Levites to slay three thousand Israelites?

174. Who was Solomon's mother?

175. What do the scriptures mean when it says a person will be cut off from among the people?

176. To whom did Ruth say, "Thy people shall be my people, and thy God my God?

177. What king offered to build a temple for the Lord?

178. What was the Mosaic law concerning a person wear-ing clothing belonging to the opposite sex?

179. Which of Joseph's brothers said, "Let us sell him [Joseph] to the Ishmeelites"?

180. What did Absalom do when he learned that his brother had raped their sister?

181. According to Isaiah, who has "transgressed the laws, changed the ordinance, and broken the everlasting covenant"?

182. Who was Bathsheba's first husband?

158. He made it float in water
(2 Kings 6:5−7)

159. Leah (Gen. 29:32−35)

160. He was hidden in the
temple (*SBD*, p. 300)

161. The "matter of Uriah the
Hittite" (1 Kings 15:5)

162. It was eaten by dogs
(2 Kings 9:35−36)

163. Jericho (*SBD*, p. 280)

164. His wife claimed that
Joseph had made advances
to her (Gen. 39:14−20)

165. Jehu (2 Kings 9, 10)

166. To prove to Israel that Levi
was the priesthood tribe
(Num. 17)

167. The pharaoh (Gen. 41:1−7)

168. Both the wingspan and
height of the cherub were
fifteen feet (1 Kings
6:23−26)

169. Three (Gen. 6:16)

170. Methuselah (Gen. 5:27)

171. Jehu (*SBD*, p. 276)

172. Daniel (Dan. 6:21−22)

173. The three thousand were
nonrepentant Israelite
rebels (Exod. 32:26−28)

174. Bathsheba (2 Sam. 12:24)

175. That person will be
excommunicated

176. Naomi (Ruth 1:11−16)

177. David (2 Sam. 7)

178. It was forbidden or an
abomination unto the Lord
(Deut. 22:5)

179. Judah (Gen. 37:26−27)

180. He killed him (2 Sam.
13:1−29)

181. The inhabitants of the earth
(Isa. 24:5)

182. Uriah (2 Sam. 11:26−27)

183. What Old Testament book title is a Greek word that means "Preacher"?

184. Within five, how many kings did the Israelites defeat when they conquered the nations of Canaan?

185. Why was Uriah sent to the "forefront of the hottest battle"?

186. Who anointed Jehu king of Israel?

187. Within one thousand, how many Levites were temple musicians during Solomon's days?

188. How many "prophets of the Lord" did Elijah hide in caves from the sword of Jezebel?

189. How large were the walls of Jericho?

190. Who was the captain of David's army?

191. What king had eighty-eight children?

192. How long was Joseph kept in an Egyptian prison?

193. What tribe of Israel was responsible for the tabernacle and its furnishings?

194. Who was the father of Absalom?

195. What creatures were enjoyed boiled, roasted, stewed, or fried in butter during Old Testament times?

196. What was the Mosaic penalty for adultery?

197. The child Samuel worshipped the Lord in the temple of what city?

198. What Israelite leader was the husband to Ahinoam, Abigail, Maacah, Haggith, Abital, and Eglah?

199. Name the first five books of the Old Testament, in order.

200. Jehoiachim, king of Judah, and his queen-mother, servants, captains, eunuchs, and harem surrendered to what foreign power?

201. What renowned Israelite judge had seventy sons?

202. Which of the following were the Israelites allowed to eat: locusts, beetles, or grasshoppers?

203. What are the Hebrew words for lights and perfections?

204. Jah, rendered "Lord" in the King James Version, is the abbreviated form of what?

205. What did David do to the two men who slew King Ishbosheth?

206. How many sons were born to Jacob?

207. What two women seduced Lot while he was drunk, hoping to become pregnant?

208. Who was the leader of David's choir and author of some of the Psalms?

183. Ecclesiastes

184. Thirty-three (Josh. 12)

185. So he would be killed
     (2 Sam. 11:15)

186. A young unnamed prophet
     under the direction of
     Elisha (2 Kings 9:1—6)

187. Four thousand (1 Chron.
     23:5)

188. One hundred (1 Kings
     18:13)

189. Large enough for homes to
     sit upon them (Josh. 2:15)

190. Joab

191. Rehoboam (2 Chron. 11:21)

192. At least two years (*SBD*,
     p. 310)

193. The Levite tribe (Num. 3, 4)

194. David (2 Sam. 3:3)

195. Locusts (*SBD*, p. 351)

196. Death by stoning (Deut.
     22:22—24)

197. Shiloh (1 Sam. 1:24)

198. King David (2 Sam. 3:2—5)

199. Genesis, Exodus, Leviticus,
     Numbers, Deuteronomy

200. Nebuchadnezzar and the
     Babylonians (*SBD*, p. 271)

201. Gideon (Judg. 8:30)

202. All three (Lev. 11:22)

203. Urim and Thummim

204. Jehovah (*SBD*, p. 264)

205. He had his soldiers slay
     them, cut off their hands
     and feet, and hang them in
     Hebron (2 Sam. 4)

206. Twelve (Gen. 35:22)

207. His daughters (Gen.
     19:30—36)

208. Asaph (*SBD*, p. 53)

209. Who cast Hagar, wife of Abraham, out of the household?

210. In the Old Testament, what was another name for the "City of David"?

211. What major prophet lived in Jerusalem at the time Lehi and his family left the city?

212. Who told the Hebrew midwives to kill every male child born to the Hebrews?

213. Who was the Egyptian handmaid of Sarah?

214. What king tried to murder three men in a fiery furnace?

215. What was the usual method of catching fish during Old Testament times?

216. Who dreamed that his parents and brothers would make obeisance to him?

217. What book title is a Greek word for *departure*?

218. Who stole Laban's idols and hid them?

219. Who was the mother of Dan and Naphtali?

220. What country conquered the Babylonians and then allowed the Jews to return to Jerusalem?

221. Who was the first son born to Adam and Eve?

222. Who was the father of eight sons, including David?

223. Who was the husband of Queen Jezebel?

224. What prophet was the son of Buzi the priest?

225. When were women caused to drink water mixed with dust from the floor of the tabernacle?

226. What caused Naomi, her husband Elimelch, and their two sons to move from Bethlehem—judah to Moab?

227. How many witnesses were required to testify against murderers in court cases?

228. What prophet became one of three presidents over the Babylonian empire?

229. When did the Israelites have a navy?

230. Who changed dust into lice?

231. Which of King David's thirty-seven bodyguards did he cause to be murdered?

232. Who put forth his hand to steady the ark, and was smitten and killed by God?

233. What did Chemosh, Astaroth, and Baalim have in common?

234. What ancient code of law said, "Eye for eye, tooth for tooth, hand for hand"?

235. What prophet said, "In the year that King Uzziah died, I saw also the Lord sitting upon a throne, high and lifted up"?

209. Sarah (Gen. 21:10−14)

210. Jerusalem (*SBD*, p. 282)

211. Jeremiah

212. The king of Egypt, the Pharaoh (Exod. 1:16)

213. Hagar (Gen. 16:1)

214. Nebuchadnezzar (Dan. 3:19−27)

215. By casting or dragging a net (*SBD*, p. 192)

216. Joseph (Gen. 37:10)

217. Exodus

218. His daughter, Rachel (Gen. 31:19, 34)

219. Bilhah (Gen. 30:5−8)

220. Persia (Ezra 1)

221. We don't know (Moses 5:2−3, 6, 11−16)

222. Jesse (*SBD*, p. 286)

223. Ahab (1 Kings 16:30−31)

224. Ezekiel (*SBD*, p. 186)

225. When they were accused of immorality (Num. 5)

226. There was a famine in Bethlehem—judah (Ruth 1:1)

227. Two or three (Deut. 19:15)

228. Daniel (Dan. 6:1−2)

229. During King Solomon's reign (1 Kings 9:26)

230. Aaron (Exod. 8:17)

231. Uriah the Hittite (*SBD*, p. 241)

232. Uzzah (2 Sam. 6:6−7)

233. They were all national deities of countries surrounding Israel (*SBD*, p. 275)

234. The law of Moses (Exod. 21:24)

235. Isaiah (Isa. 6:1)

236. Why couldn't the Israelites make their own axes, plows, spears, or swords?

237. The Jebusites were early settlers of what Israelite city?

238. Who said to the prophet Nathan, "I dwell in a house of cedar, but the ark of God dwelleth within curtains"?

239. Who said, "For out of Zion shall go forth the law, and the word of the Lord from Jerusalem"?

240. Who said, "This day will the Lord deliver thee into mine hand"?

241. What, if any, was the Mosaic penalty for victims of rape?

242. What kind of wood was Noah's ark made of?

243. What happened to the Philistines who stole the ark of the covenant?

244. Who was the plural wife of Elkanah and the mother of Samuel?

245. What unique event happened to Moses, Aaron, and seventy elders at Sinai?

246. Who interpreted the dream of the Pharaoh's chief butler?

247. What city became the first capital of the kingdom of Israel?

248. Who was the mother of Samuel?

249. Where did the Lord say he would scatter the twelve tribes of Israel?

250. What two languages could Joseph speak?

251. Who became the general of David's army by being the first man to smite the Jebusites?

252. Who was the mother of Joseph?

253. What happened to bondmen during the Year of Jubilee?

254. Who said, "For unto us a child is born, unto us a son is given"?

255. Who gave birth to twins called Esau and Jacob?

256. How often was the Israelite Year of Jubilee?

257. Who was the second wife of Abraham?

258. What Israelite king's head was mounted in the Temple of Dagon?

259. Who purchased Ruth to be his wife?

260. What were the names of Noah's three sons?

261. Who had seven hundred wives and three hundred concubines?

262. What blind man killed more than 3000 people at a religious gathering?

263. What polygamous grandson of Abraham had twelve sons and one daughter?

236. Because there was no black-smith among them (1 Sam. 13:19−20)

237. Jerusalem (*SBD*, p. 281)

238. David (2 Sam. 7:2)

239. Isaiah (Isa. 2:3)

240. David to Goliath (Sam. 17:46)

241. There was no penalty (Deut. 22:25−26)

242. Gopher wood (Gen. 6:14)

243. They were either destroyed or smitten with a plague (1 Sam. 5)

244. Hannah (1 Sam. 1:2)

245. They saw God (Exod. 24:9−10)

246. Joseph (Gen. 40:12−13)

247. Shechem (*SBD*, p. 260)

248. Hannah (1 Sam. 1:20)

249. Among all nations of the earth (Amos 9:8−9)

250. Egyptian and Hebrew (Gen. 42:23)

251. Joab (1 Chron. 11:5−6)

252. Rachel (Gen. 30:22−24)

253. They were set free (Lev. 25:8−16)

254. Isaiah (Isa. 9:6)

255. Rebekah (Gen. 25:21−26)

256. Every fiftieth year (*SBD*, p. 314)

257. Hagar (Gen. 16:3)

258. Saul's (1 Chron. 10:10)

259. Boaz (Ruth 4:9−10)

260. Shem, Ham, Japheth (Gen. 5:32)

261. Solomon (1 Kings 11:3)

262. Samson (Judg. 16:23−30)

263. Jacob (*SBD*, p. 263)

264. Who were the two celebrated sons of Amran?

265. Who wore a crown that weighed approximately seventy-five pounds?

266. What man was shaved while he was asleep?

267. Who was the second-born son of David and Bathsheba?

268. The Jebusite city of Salem is better known as what?

269. The fish-god Dagon was the principal deity of what nation?

270. Who gave Joseph a royal ring, costly vestures, and a gold chain necklace?

271. What national Israelite holiday was a fast day?

272. Which of Saul's sons became the best friend of King David?

273. Since the Levites could receive no land inheritance, how were they supported?

274. Who was a fruitful bough, "whose branches ran over the wall"?

275. What prophet wore a veil?

276. What sister of Moses spoke against him and became leprous?

277. How many of each of the clean animals did Noah take into the ark?

278. What king did Nathan the prophet call the "darling of Jehovah"?

279. Who had to shave all the hair from their bodies?

280. Who did God set a mark on, lest any finding him should kill him?

281. On what mount did Noah's ark rest after the deluge?

282. What king gave Solomon 1,200,000 shekels of gold?

283. Jebus was a city that had its name changed to what?

284. What was the greatest number of generations alive at one time?

285. Old Testament law required circumcism of every male at what age?

286. Who was the second son of Joseph and Asenath?

287. In what book is found the words, "To every thing there is a season, and a time to every purpose under the heaven"?

288. Who replaced Saul as king of Israel?

289. Who was the firstborn son of Abraham?

290. Who built temples at Dan and Bethel after the northern kingdom was established?

291. Who said it was better to dwell on the roof than with a contentious woman?

292. Who was cursed with frogs in their ovens and in their beds?

264. Aaron and Moses (Num. 26:59)

265. David (2 Sam. 12:30)

266. Samson (Judg. 16:19)

267. Solomon (2 Sam. 12:24)

268. Jerusalem (Gen. 14:18; Ps. 76:2)

269. The Philistines (1 Sam. 5:1−3)

270. Pharaoh (Gen. 41:42)

271. The Day of Atonement (*SBD*, p. 61)

272. Jonathan (*SBD*, p. 308)

273. By the tithes of the other nine tribes (Num. 18:24)

274. Joseph (Gen. 49:22)

275. Moses (Exod. 34:33)

276. Miriam (Num. 12:1−10)

277. Seven (Gen. 7:2, 5)

278. Solomon (2 Sam. 12:25)

279. Lepers (Lev. 14:9)

280. Cain (Gen. 4:15)

281. Ararat (Gen. 8:4)

282. King Hiram of Tyre (1 Kings 9:14)

283. Jerusalem (Josh. 15:8)

284. Nine (Gen. 5)

285. Eight days (Gen. 17:12)

286. Ephraim (Gen. 41:52)

287. Ecclesiastes (Eccl. 3:1)

288. David (1 Sam. 16)

289. Ishmael (Gen. 16:11−16)

290. Jeroboam (*SBD*, p. 281)

291. Solomon (Prov. 21:9)

292. The Egyptians (Exod. 8:3, 6)

293. Why were animals that were blind, broken, or maimed not allowed to be used as burnt offerings to the Lord?

294. What happened to wicked King Ahab's seventy sons?

295. What righteous woman moving her lips in silent prayer was thought by Eli to be drunk?

296. Who tried to seduce Joseph, son of Jacob?

297. Who was the father of Naphtali, Issachar, and Zebulun?

298. Who was the firstborn son of David—Solomon, Absalom, Jonathan, or Amnon?

299. What prophet saved a city by causing every man in an army to temporarily become blind?

300. Hold old was Adam when he died?

Simpler Questions for Use as Needed

301. True or false: "Honor thy father and thy mother" is one of the Ten Commandments.

302. What prophet did King Darius throw into the den of lions?

303. What did God create on the first day of creation?

304. According to the law of Moses, were the Israelites allowed to eat locusts, beetles, and grasshoppers?

305. How many sons did Israel have?

306. True or false: the first bird that Noah sent from the ark was a raven.

307. What prophet caused an axe to float in water— Elisha, Isaiah, or Jeremiah?

308. True or false: Joseph spent time in an Egyptian prison.

309. Who appeared to Moses at the burning bush?

310. What city's walls fell after the Israelites marched around it seven days?

311. Did Noah take birds on his ark?

312. What true prophet challenged 450 prophets of Baal to a contest to prove whose God was the true God?

313. What was the name of the garden where the Lord planted the tree of life?

314. Did Abraham live before or after the great flood?

315. When Aaron cast his rod down before the Pharaoh, what did the rod become—a line of fire, a stream, or a serpent?

316. What type of animal did Aaron make from gold?

293. Anything with a blemish
     was not allowed to be used
     (Lev. 22:20—22)

294. Their heads were cut off
     and sent to Jezreel (2 Kings
     10:1—7)

295. Hannah (1 Sam. 1:2—15)

296. Potiphar's wife (Gen.
     39:6—7)

297. Jacob (Gen. 30)

298. Amnon—Solomon was his
     tenth son (2 Sam. 3:2—5;
     5:14—16)

299. Elisha (2 Kings 6:8—23)

300. 930 Years (Gen. 5:5)

301. True (Exod. 20:12)

302. Daniel (Dan. 6:9—16)

303. Light (Gen. 1:3—5)

304. Yes (Lev. 11:22)

305. Twelve (Gen. 35:22)

306. True (Gen. 8:7)

307. Elisha (2 Kings 6:5)

308. True (Gen. 39:20)

309. The Lord (Exod. 3:1—7)

310. Jericho (Josh. 6:1—5)

311. Yes (Gen. 6:20)

312. Elijah (1 Kings 18:22—40)

313. Garden of Eden (Gen. 3:24)

314. After (Gen. 11:10—26)

315. A serpent (Exod. 7:10)

316. A calf (Exod. 32:1—4)

317. Who were the parents of Cain and Abel?

318. What tall building did the wicked build to reach the heavens?

319. Who built a ship of gopher wood to protect his family and countless animals?

320. What Israelite king was the richest and wisest king in all the world?

321. What happened to Shadrach, Meshach, and Abed – nego when they refused to worship Nebuchadnezzar's golden image?

322. What is the first of the Ten Commandments?

323. Who raised his rod, stretched it over the Red Sea, and parted the waters?

324. What man lost all his oxen, donkeys, sheep, camels, and servants in one day?

325. Who interpreted Pharaoh's dream of seven years of plenty and seven years of famine?

326. True or false: One of the Ten Commandments says "Thou shalt not swear."

327. True or false: When the Israelites got tired of manna in the wilderness, the Lord sent them seagulls to eat.

328. What prophet was called to preach repentance to the city of Ninevah?

329. When Balaam beat his donkey, what did the donkey do?

330. After Joseph was sold into Egypt, did he ever see his father again?

331. True or false: The clothing of the Israelites did not grow old during their forty years of wandering through the wilderness.

332. What ninety-year-old woman was told that she would bear a son — Rachel, Rebekah, Ruth, or Sarah?

333. Who or what did God send to save Daniel from the lions while he spent the night in their den?

334. What was the name of the food the Lord sent from heaven to feed the Israelites?

335. Who killed Abel?

336. What is the first book of the Bible — Moses, Exodus, Genesis, or Adam?

337. Who was given a coat of many colors?

338. What was the name of the garden where Adam and Eve first lived?

339. A prophet saw a flame of fire in a bush, and yet the bush did not burn up. Was that prophet Moses, Elijah, Isaiah, or Abraham?

340. Who spoke to the great fish, and caused it to spit Jonah upon the dry land?

317. Adam and Eve (Gen. 4:1−2)

318. The tower of Babel (Gen. 11:4−9)

319. Noah (Gen. 6:13−14)

320. Solomon (1 Kings 10:23)

321. They were cast into a fiery furnace (but they didn't burn) (Dan. 3:20−21)

322. "Thou shalt have no other gods before me" (Exod. 20:3)

323. Moses (Exod. 14:16)

324. Job (Job 1:13−19)

325. Joseph (Gen. 41:15−32)

326. False (Exod. 20:1−17)

327. False—he sent quail (Num. 11:31)

328. Jonah (Jonah 1:2)

329. It talked to him (Num. 22:27−28)

330. Yes (Gen. 46:30)

331. True (Deut. 8:4)

332. Sarah (Gen. 17:17)

333. An angel (Dan 6:22)

334. Manna (Exod. 16:31)

335. Cain (Gen. 4:8)

336. Genesis

337. Joseph (Gen. 37:3)

338. Eden (Gen. 2:15)

339. Moses (Exod. 3:1−2)

340. The Lord (Jonah 2:10)

341. Who appeared to Moses, Aaron, and seventy of the elders of Israel when they went up the mountain?

342. What sign did God set in the sky to show mankind he would never destroy them by a flood again?

343. What prophet, as a baby, was hid in the bulrushes of the Nile River?

344. True or false: Before the tower of Babel was built, everyone on the earth spoke one language.

345. When will all people live to be one hundred years old before they die?

346. Who was allowed to build the temple of Jerusalem — David or Solomon?

347. What type of animal tricked Eve into eating the fruit?

348. What weapon did David use to kill Goliath?

349. Who said, "Let there be light," and there was light?

350. What man was promised great physical strength as long as his hair was never cut?

341. The Lord (Exod. 24:9–10)

342. A rainbow (Gen. 9:13–15)

343. Moses (Exod. 2:3)

344. True (Gen. 11:1)

345. During the Millennium (Isa. 65:20)

346. Solomon (1 Chron. 17:10–13)

347. A serpent or snake (Gen. 3:1–4)

348. A sling and stone (1 Sam. 17:49)

349. God (Gen. 1:3)

350. Samson (Judg. 16:17)

PART 2 New Testament

1. At which trump will the dead be raised, according to 1 Corinthians 15:52?

2. Who will God spew out of his mouth?

3. When Joseph Smith did his inspired translation of Ephesians 1:5, 11, what did he change *predestinated* to?

4. Why does Paul say we must pay taxes?

5. How old was the girl that Jesus raised from the dead?

6. Name the father or mother of John the Baptist.

7. According to Mark, who wanted John the Baptist killed?

8. Where was Titus sent on a mission?

9. What was *corban*?

10. In what chapter of Galatians does Paul give the allegory of Isaac and Ishmael?

11. What was the hometown of of Simon and Andrew?

12. For what purpose were the scriptures written, according to Paul in writing to the Romans?

13. What does the Greek word *episkopos* mean?

14. What did Paul say we were not to touch?

15. Who was King Agrippa's father?

16. By what authority does Paul state in Romans that there are no righteous people?

17. As Paul explained in Philippians 2:12, how were the Saints to work out their salvation?

18. Where did the Essenes live?

19. What is the Hebrew word for *Master*?

20. Who said, "Is Christ divided? Was Paul crucified for you"?

21. How many epistles did Paul write to the Corinthians?

22. What is Matthew's other name?

23. What does *Bethlehem* mean?

24. If we live by the Spirit, what do we kill?

25. In what book does Paul mention "one Lord, one faith, one baptism"?

26. Luke tells us that Zacharias' wife was "of the daughters" of whom?

27. How many chapters does Galatians have?

28. How many times does the Revelation of John speak of the waters of life?

29. Paul said that who shall live by faith?

30. What epistle follows 2 Corinthians?

1. The last trump

2. Those who are lukewarm (Rev. 3:16)

3. "Foreordained"

4. All governments are God's servants (Rom. 13:6—7)

5. Twelve (Mark 5:42)

6. Zacharias and Elisabeth (Luke 1:5, 63)

7. Herodias (Mark 6:19)

8. Dalmatia (BD, p. 786)

9. Something pledged to God (Mark 7:11)

10. Four (Gal. 4:21—31)

11. Capernaum (Mark 1:29)

12. For our learning (Rom. 15:4)

13. Bishop (*BD*, p. 625)

14. "The unclean thing" (2 Cor. 6:17)

15. Herod Agrippa (BD, p. 602)

16. The scriptures (Rom. 3:10)

17. "With fear and trembling"

18. Around the Dead Sea (BD, p. 667)

19. Rabbi (BD, p. 759)

20. Paul (1 Cor. 1:13)

21. Three — 1 and 2 Corinthians and a lost epistle (See 1 Cor. 5:9)

22. Levi (Matt. 9:9; Mark 2:14)

23. House of bread (BD, p. 621)

24. Our sinful actions (Rom. 8:13, esp. Today's English Version)

25. Ephesians (Eph. 4:5)

26. Aaron (Luke 1:5)

27. Six

28. Three (Rev. 21:6; 22:1, 17)

29. The just (Rom. 1:17)

30. Galatians

31. What did Phebe do for Paul?

32. Of whom did Jesus ask where bread could be purchased before he fed the five thousand?

33. Why did Herod arrest John the Baptist?

34. What does *Thomas* mean?

35. Why didn't the wise men return to Herod?

36. What are we not to become weary of?

37. What book precedes Philippians?

38. According to Romans 1, who are self-professed wise men?

39. When Satan quoted scripture to the Lord, what Old Testament book was he quoting?

40. In which book did Paul talk most extensively about the armor of God?

41. According to Romans 3, what advantage did the Jews have over the Gentiles?

42. On what occasion did Jesus cleanse the temple for the first time?

43. Who does Paul most like to teach?

44. Who said, "There is neither Jew nor Greek"?

45. In which chapter in 1 Corinthians does Paul explain the resurrection?

46. What did Andronicus and Junia have in common with Paul?

47. According to Paul, what does the sorrow of the world work?

48. Who were Herodias's husbands?

49. Paul quotes Isaiah 8:14 about a stumbling block. What does he say the stumbling block is?

50. In what book is found the statement, "He gave some, apostles; and some, prophets"?

51. Where did John baptize Jesus?

52. What does the word *Saul* mean?

53. Over whom was Mary told Christ would rule?

54. What is Aenon known for?

55. What mountain is Bethany on?

56. What was the nationality of most of Paul's early converts in Corinth?

57. Where was Paul when he wrote the book of Romans?

58. Which two covenants did Paul compare in Galatians 4?

31. She delivered his letter to the Romans (Endnote to Romans)

32. Philip (John 6:5)

33. For condemning his marriage to Herodias (Matt. 14:3−4)

34. Twin (BD, p. 657)

35. God warned them in a dream (Matt. 2:12)

36. "Well-doing" (Gal. 6:9)

37. Ephesians

38. Fools (Rom. 1:22)

39. Psalms (Ps. 91:11; see also Matt. 4:6)

40. Ephesians (Eph. 6:10−20)

41. The oracles (prophets) of God (Rom. 3:1−2)

42. During the first Passover of his ministry (John 2:13−17)

43. Those who have not heard of the Lord (Rom. 15:20)

44. Paul (Gal. 3:28)

45. 1 Corinthians 15

46. They were Christians who were imprisoned with him (Rom. 16:7)

47. Death (2 Cor. 7:10)

48. Herod Philip and Herod Antipas (BD, p. 702)

49. Living by works, and not faith (Rom. 9:32−33)

50. Ephesians (Eph. 4:11)

51. Bethabara (John 1:28−29)

52. "Asked for" (*Strong's Hebrew Dictionary*, No. 7586)

53. The house of Jacob (Luke 1:33)

54. John performed baptisms there (John 3:23)

55. Olivet (BD, p. 621)

56. Greek (BD, p. 734)

57. Corinth (Endnote to Romans)

58. The law of Moses and the law of the gospel (Gal. 4:22−31)

59. How many chapters are contained in the Revelation of John?

60. According to Paul, believers are not under the law, but they are under what?

61. How many chapters does James have?

62. Where do we learn that Paul is the author of 1 Corinthians?

63. What is written on the white stone mentioned in Revelation 2:17?

64. Which Old Testament prophet did Paul quote in saying, "Death is swallowed up in victory"?

65. According to Romans 1, God reveals himself to all men by what?

66. Which pagan goddess had a temple in Ephesus?

67. What does Peter mean?

68. What type of tree did Christ curse?

69. Name one of the pastoral epistles.

70. Where did Paul say his fathers were baptized?

71. According to tradition, who was the only Apostle to escape a violent death?

72. How far was it from Bethlehem to Jerusalem?

73. What did the Lord say to the man lowered through the roof that upset the scribes?

74. What does Boanerges mean?

75. What modern country was the Roman province of Macedonia?

76. How long are we subject to the law, according to Paul?

77. What is the main theme of Galatians?

78. Who is the first Comforter?

79. Over what people did Paul feel continual sorrow?

80. What was the occupation of Cornelius?

81. Where did King Agrippa hear Paul's defense?

82. What Roman province did the Samaritans live in — Judea, Decapolis, Perea, or Galilee?

83. What prompted Paul's epistle to the Galatians?

84. What modern country was the Roman province of Asia?

85. What shall he that overcometh be clothed in?

86. How many chapters are in the book of 1 Corinthians?

87. How many righteous does Paul say there are?

88. Who was the first of the original Apostles to die?

89. According to Ephesians 4, how long will the Saints have apostles and prophets?

90. What was Aceldama?

59. Twenty-two

60. Grace (Rom. 6:14)

61. Five

62. 1 Corinthians 1:1

63. A new name

64. Isaiah (1 Cor. 15:54; Isa. 25:8)

65. The things that are made (Rom. 1:20)

66. Artemis (Diana) (Acts 9:35)

67. Stone or rock (BD, p. 749)

68. Fig (Mark 11:12−14)

69. Titus, 1 Timothy and 2 Timothy (BD, p. 747)

70. In the cloud and in the sea (1 Cor. 10:1−2)

71. John the Beloved (*Missionary Pal*, p. 10)

72. Five miles (BD, p. 621)

73. "Thy sins are forgiven thee" (Mark 2:5−7)

74. Sons of thunder (Mark 3:17)

75. Greece (BG)

76. As long as we live (Rom. 8:11)

77. The gospel is superior to the law of Moses (BD, p. 734)

78. The Holy Ghost (BD, p. 648)

79. The descendants of Abraham (Rom. 9:2−5)

80. He was a Roman centurion (Acts 10:1)

81. Caesarea (BD, p. 605)

82. Judea (BG, Map 14)

83. The news of widespread apostasy (BD, p. 744)

84. Turkey (BG, Map 13)

85. White raiment (Rev. 3:5)

86. Sixteen

87. None (Rom. 3:10)

88. Judas (Matt. 27:3−5)

89. "Till we all come in the unity of the faith" (Eph. 4:13)

90. The field Judas Iscariot bought (*BD*, p. 602)

91. According to Romans 2, what is the "goodness of God" for?

92. Why should a man not cover his head when praying?

93. According to Romans 1, to whom was Paul called as an Apostle?

94. Who has the right to partake of the tree of life, as as explained in Revelation 22:14?

95. Where does Paul mention the three degrees of glory?

96. Who baptized Paul?

97. When Paul said, "I have planted," who did he say had watered?

98. Who was the first known Gentile baptized in the Church without first becoming a Jew?

99. Name one of the two reasons the Jews sought to kill Jesus, as recorded in John 5.

100. Who in the New Testament said, "Prove all things; hold fast that which is good"?

101. How many pots of water did the Lord change into wine?

102. What are the wages of sin?

103. Paul said that the letter killeth. What does the Spirit give?

104. What modern country is Corinth in?

105. How much leaven does it take to leaven the whole lump?

106. Where do we read, "For God so loved the world that he gave his only begotten son . . . "?

107. How many Passovers during Christ's ministry are mentioned in John?

108. What descriptive name is given to the epistles to Timothy and Titus?

109. What was the schoolmaster to bring the people to Christ?

110. Who did John the Baptist call a "generation of vipers"?

111. What surname did Jesus give James and John?

112. What is the Hebrew word for Calvary?

113. On what were most of Paul's epistles likely written?

114. What is the other name of the Apostle Simon (not Simon Peter)?

115. In what book did Paul speak of being caught up to the third heaven?

116. How many Beatitudes are recorded in Matthew 5?

117. What did John the Baptist say the Lord would baptize with?

118. Who did Paul encourage the Corinthian Saints to see regarding lawsuits?

91. To lead us to repentance (Rom. 2:4)

92. He is the image and glory of God (1 Cor. 11:7)

93. All nations (Rom. 1:5)

94. Those who keep God's commandments

95. 1 Corinthians 15

96. Ananias (Acts 9:10–18)

97. Apollos (1 Cor. 3:6)

98. Cornelius (BD, p. 651)

99. Healing on the Sabbath, and saying God was his father (John 5:18)

100. Paul (1 Thess. 5:21)

101. Six (John 2:6–7)

102. Death (Rom. 6:23)

103. Life (2 Cor. 3:6)

104. Greece (BG, Map 20)

105. Only "a little" (1 Cor. 5:6; Gal. 5:9)

106. John 3:16

107. Three (*HH*, p. 161)

108. Pastoral (BD, p. 742)

109. The law of Moses (Gal. 3:24)

110. The Sadducees and Pharisees (Matt. 3:7)

111. Boanerges (Mark 3:17)

112. Golgotha (BD, p. 629)

113. Papyrus (BD, p. 790)

114. Zelotes (Luke 6:15)

115. 2 Corinthians (2 Cor. 12:2–4)

116. Nine (Matt. 5:3–12)

117. The Holy Ghost and with fire (Matt. 3:11)

118. The other Saints (1 Cor. 6)

119. Who was Eutychus?

120. What did John the Baptist tell the tax collectors who asked him, "What shall we do"?

121. Name one of the four bearers of the epistle to the Corinthians.

122. In what book did Paul ask, "Know ye not that ye are the temple of God"?

123. Alphaeus was the father of which Apostle?

124. How far was it from Bethany to Jerusalem?

125. Paul said our sufferings were not worthy to be compared with what?

126. Name one of the groups Paul said he was obligated or in debt to.

127. In Matthew's genealogical record of Jesus, how many generations were there from Abraham to David?

128. In Luke's genealogical record of Jesus, how many generations were there between Adam and Jesus (within five)?

129. Who founded the city of Antipatris?

130. How was Paul killed?

131. What did the Roman captain Claudius Lysias do for Paul?

132. Who was the servant of the church at Cenchrea?

133. What kind of loaves were used to feed the five thousand?

134. Of whom does the verse speak that says, "I shall send my messenger before thy face which shall prepare thy way before thee"?

135. What was a person from Nazareth called?

136. Paul taught the Corinthians that tongues were a sign for whom?

137. In what book did Paul first use the term "New Testament"?

138. What was the name of the man who carried Paul's epistle to the Colossians?

139. To whom did James direct his epistle?

140. Paul said the epistles to the Corinthians were written not with ink but with what?

141. What does the word *baptize* mean?

142. When Jesus fed the five thousand, how many baskets of food were left?

143. Who wrote, "For there is no respect of persons with God," and who did he write it to?

144. In Romans 16, who did Paul teach that we should avoid?

145. Who was the president of the Sanhedrin?

119. A boy Paul raised from the dead (Acts 20:9)

120. Take no more tax than you are told (Luke 3:13)

121. Stephanas or Fortunatus or Achaicus or Timotheus (See note at end of 1 Cor.)

122. 1 Corinthians (1 Cor. 3:16)

123. James (BD, p. 606)

124. Two miles (BD, p. 621)

125. Our future glory (Rom. 8:18)

126. Greeks and non-Greeks, learned and unlearned (Rom. 1:14)

127. Fourteen (Matt. 1:17)

128. Seventy-five (Luke 2:23–38)

129. Herod the Great (BD, p. 609)

130. Beheaded by order of Nero (*Missionary Pal*, p. 10)

131. He rescued Paul from a murderous mob of Jews (BD, p. 646)

132. Phebe (Rom. 16:1)

133. Barley (John 6:5)

134. John the Baptist (Luke 7:27)

135. A Nazarene (not a Nazarite, which was something else) (BD, p. 737)

136. Unbelievers (1 Cor. 14:22)

137. 2 Corinthians (2 Cor. 3:6)

138. Tychicus

139. The twelve tribes scattered abroad (BD, p. 709)

140. "The Spirit of the living God" (2 Cor. 3:3)

141. To dip or immerse (*BD*, p. 618)

142. Twelve (Matt. 14:20)

143. Paul, to the Romans (Rom. 2:11)

144. Those who go against Christ's teachings (Rom. 16:17)

145. The high priest (BD, p. 769)

146. How many men were in a Roman legion?

147. What were John the Baptist's clothes made of?

148. How many Roman soldiers watched the crucifixion?

149. According to Romans, for whose sake are the Jews enemies of God?

150. In what epistle did Paul compare the members of the Church to the parts of a human body?

151. What is the Hebrew equivalent of the Greek word *Didymus*?

152. What does *Apostle* mean?

153. How did Elisabeth know Mary was the mother of the Lord?

154. What New Testament character was mistaken for the god Jupiter?

155. What does *Gethsemane* mean?

156. How many sisters did Jesus have?

157. When the Lord cast out Legion into the herd of swine, how many swine were there?

158. After explaining in Galatians 5 that the Saints are to serve one another, what saying of Jesus did Paul repeat?

159. What did the phrase "by and by" mean when the King James Version was translated?

160. What was Peter's surname?

161. What happened to the Church in Thessalonica between Paul's first and second epistles to them?

162. Why did the Lord give Apostles, prophets, and evangelists to the Church?

163. What does the word *abba* mean?

164. What was the new Hebrew name given to Simon Peter by Jesus?

165. Where did Paul go when he left Damascus?

166. Who did Peter want to make three tabernacles for on the Mount of Transfiguration?

167. How many Passovers during Christ's ministry are explicitly mentioned in the Synoptic Gospels?

168. What is the only book to tell of Jesus' flight into Egypt?

169. Name two of the fruits of the Spirit, as taught in Galatians 5.

170. In Philippians 1, what is the name of the man who seems to be one of Paul's most trusted assistants?

171. Name two Old Testament prophets who prophesied of many of the same things as does the Revelation of John?

146. Six thousand (BD, p. 632)

147. Camel hair (Mark 1:16)

148. Four (BD, p. 651)

149. The Gentiles (Rom. 11:27)

150. 1 Corinthians (1 Cor. 12)

151. Thomas (BD, p. 657)

152. One sent forth (BD, p. 612)

153. Her baby (John the Baptist) leaped in her womb (Luke 1:44)

154. Barnabas (Acts 14:12)

155. [Olive] oil press (*Strong's Greek Dictionary*, No. 1068)

156. At least two (Matt. 13:55)

157. About two thousand (Mark 5:13)

158. "Thou shalt love one another as thyself " (Gal. 5:14)

159. Immediately (BD, p. 627)

160. Bar-jona (son of Jonah or son of John) (Matt. 16:17)

161. Members suffered persecution (BD, p. 743)

162. "For the perfecting of the saints" (Eph. 4:12)

163. Father (BD, p. 600)

164. Cephas (John 1:42)

165. To Jerusalem (Gal. 1:18)

166. Jesus, Moses, Elias (Luke 9:33

167. One (*HH*, p. 161)

168. Matthew (*HH*, p. 10)

169. Love, joy, peace, long-suffering, gentleness, goodness, and faith

170. Timothy (Philip. 1:20–23)

171. Amos, Isaiah, Jeremiah, Ezekiel, and Daniel (BD, p. 762)

172. With what are the pastoral epistles generally concerned?

173. According to Paul, how should liberty be used?

174. What is another name for the Sea of Galilee?

175. The name *Gabriel* appears only twice in the New Testament. Where?

176. To whom did Paul write "[God] will render to every man according to his deeds"?

177. Who was scribe for Paul's letter to the Romans?

178. What was the farthest north Christ traveled during his lifetime?

179. What was the hometown of Matthew?

180. How many chapters does Ephesians have?

181. What was the Sanhedrin?

182. To what period of time did Paul refer when he mentioned the "dispensation of the fulness of times"?

183. In Revelation 1:8, what do "Alpha and Omega" mean?

184. Of what race were the Grecians?

185. In the New Testament, who are the damned?

186. What did Paul teach would be the last enemy to be destroyed?

187. Who ministered to the Lord after the great temptations?

188. Paul told the Galatians that if they were the Lord's they were the seed of whom?

189. Who succeeded Felix as procurator of Judea?

190. What tribe of Israel was Barnabas from?

191. What is the foundation of the Church, as we read in Ephesians 2?

192. Where was the term *Christians* first used?

193. Paul gives us this formula: Predestinate, call, justify, glorify. In what book do we find it?

194. Where did the Colossians live?

195. Where does Paul mention baptism for the dead?

196. Who baptized Crispus, Gaius, and the household of Stephanas at Corinth?

197. Of what group does the scripture speak that says, "For the name of God is blasphemed among the gentiles through you"?

198. What did Simon of Cyrene do for Jesus?

199. As noted in Galatians, where did Paul go after his conversion?

200. What disease did the man that was lowered from a hole in the roof have?

172. Church discipline and organization (BD, p. 748)

173. To serve one another (Gal. 5:13)

174. Lake Gennesaret (*BD*, p. 679)

175. Luke, chapter 1 (*Strong's Exhaustive Concordance*)

176. The Romans (Rom. 2:16)

177. Tertius (Rom. 16:22)

178. Caesarea Philippi (BD, p. 628)

179. Capernaum (Matt. 9:9)

180. Six

181. The Jewish senate and high court (BD, p. 769)

182. The last days, from Joseph Smith to the Millennium (Eph. 1:10)

183. The beginning and the end

184. Jewish (BD, p. 697)

185. Everyone who is not exalted (BD, p. 652)

186. Death (1 Cor. 15:26)

187. Angels (Matt. 4:11)

188. Abraham (Gal. 3:29)

189. Festus (BD, p. 674)

190. Levi (Acts 4:35)

191. "Apostles and prophets" (Eph. 2:20)

192. Antioch (Acts 11:26)

193. Romans (Rom. 8:30)

194. Colossae (Col. 1:2)

195. 1 Corinthians 15(1 Cor. 15:29)

196. Paul (1 Cor. 1:14,16)

197. The Jews (Rom. 2:17−24)

198. Bore his cross (Matt. 27:32)

199. "Into Arabia" (Gal. 1:17)

200. Palsy (Mark 2:1−4)

201. According to Galatians, who are the children of Abraham?

202. When the New Testament says the Lord "went into his own city," what city is being referred to?

203. In Revelation, what did John see when the first seal was opened?

204. Who was with Paul when he wrote 2 Corinthians?

205. How many men did a centurion command?

206. Where did the disciples get the donkey Jesus rode into Jerusalem?

207. What English word is derived from the Greek word for *revelation*?

208. In which book did Paul say, "We wrestle not against flesh and blood"?

209. Where does the Revelation of John say the tree of life is?

210. Who did Paul say the Saints should not be unequally yoked with?

211. Why did Mary and Joseph go to Jerusalem on the occasion when they lost Jesus?

212. What is the only Gospel with the story of Zacharias in it?

213. How are the New Testament epistles organized?

214. How many chapters are in 2 Corinthians?

215. Which of Paul's epistles was written earliest?

216. How many cities by the name of Bethsaida were there at the time of Jesus?

217. What does our "reasonable service" represent to God?

218. What was the social standing of Onesimus, who is discussed in Philemon?

219. Who was the father of Archelaus?

220. What city was the Apostle Philip from?

221. What did Paul teach that every woman who prays or prophesies should do?

222. Who was Agabus?

223. What does the word *alleluia* (*hallelujah*) mean?

224. In what city did Jesus change the water to wine?

225. According to Romans 8, how does the Spirit help us when we pray?

226. Paul taught that "he who judges others judges himself." Why is this so?

227. According to Paul, what phrase can all commandments be summarized by?

228. What modern Article of Faith comes from Philippians 4?

229. Why did Paul suggest that the Saints allow themselves to be defrauded?

201. "They which are of faith" (Gal. 3:7)

202. Capernaum (BD, p. 631)

203. A white horse (Rev. 6:2)

204. Timothy (2 Cor. 1:1)

205. One hundred (BD, p . 632)

206. Bethphage (Matt. 21:21, 22)

207. Apocalypse (BD, p. 762)

208. Ephesians (Eph. 6:12)

209. "In the midst of paradise" (Rev. 2:7)

210. Unbelievers (2 Cor. 6:14)

211. For the Passover (Luke 2:41)

212. Luke (*HH*)

213. Generally by length (BD, p. 743)

214. Thirteen

215. 1 Thessalonians (BD, p. 743)

216. Two (BD, p. 625)

217. A "living sacrifice" (Rom. 12:1)

218. He was a slave (BD, p. 746)

219. Herod the Great (Matt. 2:22)

220. Bethsaida (John 1:44)

221. Have her head covered (1 Cor. 11:5)

222. A prophet who foretold famine and Paul's imprisonment (Acts 11:28; 21:10)

223. "Praise ye the Lord" or "Praise Jehovah" (BD, 606)

224. Cana (John 2:1)

225. He intercedes for us according to God's will (Rom. 8:27)

226. The "judge" is guilty of the same offense (Rom. 2:1)

227. Love thy neighbor as thyself (Rom. 13:9)

228. Article of Faith 13 (Phil. 4:8)

229. He felt it was better to be defrauded than to risk unrighteousness (1 Cor. 6:6−7)

230. Who compared life to a race?

231. What did Paul feed the Corinthians, speaking symbolically?

232. In the letter to the Romans, when did Paul say he planned to leave for Spain?

233. To which churches was Paul "unknown by face"?

234. Who said to Jesus, "Dost thou not care that my sister hath left me to serve alone"?

235. Which of Paul's epistles did he write just before his martyrdom?

236. What is the second longest of the Pauline epistles?

237. What does the word *gospel* mean?

238. Paul asked the Roman believers to pray for his safety from whom?

239. Paul tells the Romans that being made free from sin they become the servants of what?

240. Why is the epistle to the Hebrews placed at the end of Paul's epistles?

241. Where was Cornelius baptized?

242. How many "churches in Asia" did John write to in his revelation?

243. What is the main theme of Hebrews 11?

244. Where was Paul when he wrote to the Philippians?

245. What power does Paul say the gospel of Christ is?

246. In Galatians 5, Paul taught that faith works by what?

247. In which chapter and book did Paul explain that "as in Adam all die, even so in Christ shall all be made alive?"

248. According to Paul, what is a "true Jew"?

249. How many men did the Sanhedrin consist of— thrity, seventy, seventy-one, or one hundred?

250. How was Peter killed?

251. What does *Barabbas* mean?

252. What pagan god was Paul mistaken for?

253. The word *church* is translated from the Greek word *ecclesia*. What does it mean?

254. What Old Testament prophet did the Lord quote when he announced his Messiahship to the people of Nazareth?

255. How many porches did the pool of Bethesda have?

256. Who wrote the book of Acts?

257. Which of Paul's epistles was written last?

230. Paul (1 Cor. 9:24)

231. Milk (1 Cor. 3:2)

232. After delivering money from Greece to Jerusalem (Rom. 15:25−28)

233. The churches of Judaea (Gal. 1:22)

234. Martha (Luke 10:40)

235. 2 Timothy (BD, p. 748)

236. 1 Corinthians

237. Good news (BD, p. 682)

238. Disbelieving Jews (Rom. 15:31)

239. Righteousness (Rom. 6:18)

240. Because there was some disputation as to Paul's authorship (BD, p. 743)

241. Caesarea (BD, p. 628)

242. Seven (Rev. 1:4)

243. Faith

244. Rome (See endnote to Philippians)

245. The power unto salvation for believers (Rom. 1:16)

246. Love (Gal. 5:6)

247. 1 Corinthians 15 (1 Cor. 15:22)

248. A person who inwardly keeps the law (Rom. 2:25−29)

249. Seventy-one (BD, p. 769)

250. He was crucified (tradition says upside down) (*Missionary Pal*, p. 10)

251. Son of the father (BD, p. 619)

252. Mercury (Acts 14:12)

253. An assembly called together (BD, p. 645)

254. Isaiah (Luke 4:18−19; see Isa. 61:1−2)

255. Five (Matt. 5:2)

256. Luke (Acts 1:1; Luke 1:4)

257. 2 Timothy (BD, p. 743)

258. What was Paul's main teaching in 2 Thessalonians?

259. According to Paul, what was "God's building"?

260. Where was John when he received his great revelation?

261. How many chapters are there in 1 John?

262. In which book did Paul encourage the Saints to seek after spiritual gifts and prophecy?

263. Where was 1 Corinthians written from?

264. According to Paul, how many Israelites committed fornication and "fell in one day"?

265. What does *Emmanuel* mean?

266. In Ephesians 4, who are the Saints encouraged not to give place to?

267. What distinguished the centurion in Capernaum whose servant the Lord healed?

268. In what Gospel is the miracle of changing water to wine recorded?

269. To what group of people was the Gospel of Matthew written?

270. By what title does John refer to the Lord in the beginning of his Gospel?

271. How many major changes did Joseph Smith make in Philippians 1?

272. What books are called the Synoptic Gospels?

273. To whom is the book of Romans addressed?

274. In what city did the Lord raise a widow's son from the dead?

275. Where was Jesus when the "woman caught in adultery" was brought to him?

276. What brought death into the world, according to Paul?

277. Who is the chief cornerstone of the Church?

278. Who said he was the "least of the apostles"?

279. What is the shortest epistle in the New Testament?

280. What does the natural man consider foolishness?

281. Who carried Paul's first and second epistles to the Corinthians?

282. What book and chapter is devoted to charity?

283. On what conditions are we "of all men most miserable"?

284. How long after the Jews asked John the Baptist if he was the Christ was the Lord baptized?

258. The Lord was not to return immediately (BD, p. 743)

259. Members of the Church (1 Cor. 3:9)

260. In exile on the isle of Patmos (Rev. 1:9)

261. Five

262. 1 Corinthians (1 Cor. 14)

263. Philippi (See endnote to 1 Cor.)

264. 23,000 (1 Cor. 10:8)

265. God with us (Matt. 1:23)

266. The devil (Eph. 4:27)

267. His faith exceeded that of any in Israel (Matt. 8:10; Luke 7:9)

268. John (HH)

269. The Jews (HH, p. v)

270. The Word (John 1:1−14)

271. One (Philip. 1:28)

272. Matthew, Mark, Luke (BD, p. 715)

273. To all who live in Rome (Rom. 1:7)

274. Nain (Luke 7:11)

275. At the temple (John 8:2−4)

276. Sin (Rom. 5:12)

277. The Lord (Eph. 2:20)

278. Paul (1 Cor. 15:9)

279. Philemon

280. "The things of the Spirit of God" (1 Cor. 2:14)

281. Titus (BD, p. 786)

282. 1 Corinthians 13

283. If we have no hope in Christ in the next life (1 Cor. 15:19)

284. One day (John 1:19−32)

285. According to Paul, the Jews required a sign — and what did the Greeks seek after?

286. Who or what was Easter originally?

287. Within ten years, in what year did Palestine come under Roman power?

288. Where was Barabbas born?

289. What Book of Mormon prophet had an experience similar to John the Revelator's "guided tour" by an angel?

290. What is "Abraham's bosom"?

291. When the messenger bore Paul's epistle to the Ephesians, what other epistle did he also carry?

292. Who said, "God is faithful, who will not suffer you to be tempted above that ye are able"?

293. According to Paul, we are buried with Christ by what?

294. Who converted Titus?

295. With what are the Saints sealed after they believe?

296. In which book is the following: "Now therefore ye are no more strangers and foreigners but fellowcitizens with the saints"?

297. Who was Paul's host when he wrote Romans?

298. Who gave help to the poor Christians in Jerusalem?

299. How long had the woman who was healed by touching Jesus' robe been suffering?

300. What proof did the Lord offer that he could forgive sins?

Simpler Questions for Use as Needed

301. What gifts were given to Jesus by the wise men?

302. What word does each of the Beatitudes begin with?

303. How much food did Jesus start with when he fed the five thousand?

304. Who or what rolled the stone away from the tomb where Jesus was laid after his crucifixion?

305. How many people did Jesus feed with only five loaves of bread and two fishes?

306. When the soldiers came to get Jesus, what did Peter do to protect him?

307. What town was Jesus born in?

308. What caused death to come into the world?

285. Wisdom (1 Cor. 1:22)

286. A Norse pagan goddess (BD, p. 659)

287. 63 B.C. (BD, p. 763)

288. Cyprus (Acts 4:36)

289. Nephi (BD, pp. 762–63)

290. The place of the righteous dead (BD, p. 602)

291. Colossians (BD, p. 746.)

292. Paul (1 Cor. 10:13)

293. Baptism (Rom. 6:4)

294. Paul (Titus 1:4 and BD, p. 785)

295. "The holy Spirit of promise" (Eph. 1:13)

296. Ephesians (Eph. 2:19)

297. Gaius (Rom. 16:23)

298. The Saints of Macedonia and Achaia (Rom. 15:26)

299. Twelve years (Matt. 9:20)

300. Healing a man of the palsy (Matt. 9:5–6)

301. Gold, frankincense, and myrrh (Matt. 2:11)

302. Blessed (Matt. 5:3–11)

303. Five loaves and two fishes (Matt. 14:17)

304. An angel (Matt. 28:2)

305. Five thousand (Matt. 14:17–21)

306. He pulled his sword and cut off the ear of one of the Jews (Matt. 26:51)

307. Bethlehem (Matt. 2:1)

308. Adam and Eve ate the fruit in the Garden of Eden (1 Cor. 15:21–22)

309. Who wrote most of the books in the New Testament—John, Paul, Matthew, or James?

310. How old was Jesus when he was baptized—eight, ten, fifteen, or thirty?

311. How old was the girl that Jesus brought back from the dead—nine, ten, eleven, or twelve?

312. Who told Joseph that Mary's baby would become the Savior of the world?

313. In the New Testament, who taught us how to pray?

314. Joseph and Mary took the baby Jesus to a foreign country to save him from the king. Did they take him to Arabia, Turkey, Egypt, or Greece?

315. Who was the first person ever to be resurrected?

316. How long did Jesus fast in the desert—three days, ten days, twenty-five days, or forty days?

317. "Blessed are the pure in heart, for they shall see_____"

318. When Jesus entered Jerusalem for the last time, what did he ride on?

319. Jesus taught that the kingdom of heaven was like what kind of pearl?

320. What did Peter do for a living—was he a tax collector, a carpenter, a fisherman, or farmer?

321. What was Paul's calling in the Church?

322. When the devil tempted Jesus, what did he tell Jesus to turn a stone into?

323. Who was the first person to see Jesus after he was resurrected—Peter, John, Mary Magdalene, or Paul?

324. Name one of the two things the Jews did to safeguard the tomb where Jesus was laid after he was crucified.

325. Did Jesus have any brothers or sisters?

326. What is the first book in the New Testament?

327. How many New Testament books did Jude write—one, two, or three?

328. Who named John the Baptist—his father, his mother, the priest, or an angel?

329. When John the Baptist lived in the desert, what did he eat for meat—rabbit, snake, sheep, or locusts?

330. When Jesus walked on the water, which Apostle walked on the water to meet him?

331. At a wedding celebration, what did Jesus turn water into?

332. Does the book of Revelation deal mainly with the past, the present, or the future?

333. Who was tempted, but never sinned?

309. Paul

310. Thirty (Luke 3:21−23)

311. Twelve (Mark 5:35−42)

312. An angel (Matt. 1:20−21)

313. Jesus (Matt. 6:9−13)

314. Egypt (Matt. 2:13)

315. Jesus (Col. 1:18)

316. Forty days (Luke 4:2)

317. "God" (Matt. 5:8)

318. A colt (Mark 11:2−10)

319. A pearl of great price (Matt. 13:46)

320. A fisherman (Matt. 4:18)

321. Apostle (2 Cor. 1:1)

322. Bread (Luke 4:3)

323. Mary Magdalene (John 20:11−16)

324. They had a stone rolled in front of the tomb opening, and they got Roman soldiers to guard the tomb (Matt. 27:62−66)

325. Yes (Matt. 13:55)

326. Matthew

327. One

328. An angel (Luke 1:13)

329. Locusts (Mark 1:6)

330. Peter (Matt. 14:25−29)

331. Wine (John 2:1−9)

332. The future

333. Jesus (Heb. 4:15)

334. What did Judas do to show the Roman soldiers which man was Jesus?

335. "Blessed are the meek, for they shall inherit the_____"

336. Who was the Roman governor who let the Romans and Jews crucify Jesus?

337. What book comes after the book of Luke?

338. Name four of the original Twelve Apostles.

339. What town did Jesus grow up in — Bethlehem, Jerusalem, Nazareth, or Cana?

340. Who will resurrect us?

341. What did Jesus teach was the greatest of all commandments?

342. What did Jesus do when he found wicked money-changers in the temple?

343. What righteous prophet had his head cut off by wicked King Herod?

344. Who baptized Jesus?

345. What king tried to kill the baby Jesus?

346. Who wrote the book of Revelation — Matthew, Mark, Luke, or John?

347. Which of the Twelve Apostles betrayed Jesus to the Roman soldiers?

348. Who first told Mary Magdalene that Jesus had been resurrected — Peter, John, an angel, or Jesus himself?

349. When Jesus was resurrected, who else was resurrected with him?

350. What did Joseph, husband of Mary, do for a living?

334. He kissed Jesus on the cheek (Matt. 26:46–48)

335. "Earth" (Matt. 5:5)

336. Pontius Pilate (Matt. 27:22–26)

337. John

338. Peter, Andrew, James, John, Philip, Bartholomew, Thomas, Matthew, James (son of Alphaeus), Thaddaeus, Simon, Judas Iscariot (Matt. 10:2–4)

339. Nazareth (Matt. 2:23)

340. Jesus (2 Cor. 4:14)

341. To love God (Matt. 22:36–38)

342. He cast them out (Mark 11:15)

343. John the Baptist (Matt. 14:3–10)

344. John the Baptist (Matt. 3:13–16)

345. Herod (Matt. 2:13)

346. John

347. Judas Iscariot (Matt. 26:46–47)

348. An angel (Mark 16:5–6)

349. The righteous who had died before that time (Matt. 27:52–53)

350. He was a carpenter (Matt. 13:55)

PART **3**   Book of Mormon

1. Abinadi prophesied that the life of King Noah would be valued as a garment in a_____.

2. Who said, "To me he doth not stink"?

3. Which one of the eight Witnesses was neither a Smith nor a Whitmer?

4. Apart from elephants, what two animals were especially useful to the Jaredites of Emer's day?

5. What was the ratio of people to priests appointed by Alma the elder in Mormon?

6. Who is the first prophet who wrote in the Book of Mormon?

7. Why did Nephi's brothers run away from him when he approached with Zoram and the brass plates?

8. Why did Lehi's sons give their gold and silver to Laban?

9. Who did Nephi prophesy would cry, "A Bible! A Bible! We have got a Bible"?

10. Who would not believe Alma's words when they saw Corianton's bad conduct?

11. What book in the Book of Mormon has five different authors?

12. What did the Jaredites call the Hill Cumorah?

13. Who raised his brother Timothy from the dead?

14. What did King Mosiah discover was written on the twenty-four gold plates found by Limhi's people?

15. Name one of the three companions of Ammon who were thrown into prison by King Limhi.

16. Why was the title page of the Book of Mormon not lost with the 116 manuscript pages?

17. Who was Lehi's wife?

18. Whose sons each refused to become the king of the Jaredites?

19. 2 Nephi 30:6 used to read: "They shall become a white and delightsome people." How was that corrected in the 1981 edition?

20. Which antichrist in the Book of Mormon was executed?

21. Why was Nehor executed?

22. Who preached to the Nephites from the walls of the city of Zarahemla?

23. Who commanded the Nephite armies against Giddianhi?

24. How was the name of the city of Bountiful different from the cities of Zarahemla, Morianton, Manti, and Moroni?

25. If there are faults in the Book of Mormon, whose mistakes are they?

1. Furnace (Mosiah 12:3, 10)

2. King Lamoni's wife (Alma 19:5)

3. Hiram Page

4. Cureloms and cumoms (Eth. 9:19)

5. One priest to fifty people (Mosiah 18:18)

6. Nephi (1 Ne. 1:1)

7. They thought he was Laban (1 Ne. 4:28)

8. To try to buy the brass plates (1 Ne. 3:24)

9. Gentiles (2 Ne. 29:13)

10. The Zoramites (Alma 39:11)

11. Omni

12. Ramah (Eth. 15:11)

13. Nephi (3 Ne. 7:19; 19:4)

14. An account of the Jaredites (Mosiah 28:17)

15. Amaleki, Helem, Hem (Mosiah 7:6)

16. It was translated from the last plate (*TPJS*, p. 7)

17. Sariah (1 Ne. 2:5)

18. The brother of Jared's (Eth. 6:25)

19. To "*pure* and delightsome"

20. Nehor (Alma 1:15)

21. For killing Gideon (Alma 1:9–15)

22. Samuel the Lamanite (Hel. 13–15)

23. Gidgiddoni (3 Ne. 3:18)

24. Bountiful was not named after a person

25. Men's (Title page of the Book of Mormon)

26. To what kind of stone did Nephi compare the hearts of the Lamanites?

27. Whose blood was discovered on the skirts of his brother?

28. Who was king of Zarahemla when the people of Limhi arrived after their escape from the Lamanites?

29. How many Lamanites did Ammon kill in defense of King Lamoni's flocks?

30. Who did Nephi prophesy would carry the Book of Mormon to his descendants?

31. What was to be the purpose of the ensign to be established by the Lord as prophesied in 2 Nephi 21:12?

32. From what Book of Mormon prophet do we learn that Lehi was descended from Manasseh?

33. With whom did the people of Morianton contend?

34. Who said, "O be wise; what can I say more?

35. How many sons of Ishmael accompanied Lehi and his family?

36. Who accused Lehi of being a visionary man?

37. From which tribe of Israel was Lehi descended?

38. To whom did Ammon bind himself as a servant?

39. Who was the son of Jacob?

40. How did Nephi kill Laban?

41. Who was the leader of King Noah's priests in the wilderness?

42. To whom in the Book of Mormon did the Lord say, "And never have I showed myself unto man whom I have created"?

43. Who did King Limhi suppose Ammon and his brethren to be?

44. What was it that caused Zoram to realize it was not Laban for whom he was carrying the brass plates?

45. Who is the major Nephite prophet in the Book of Helaman?

46. From whom was the Lamanite general Coriantumr descended?

47. Who prayed that Alma the younger would repent?

48. To what did the Lord compare "a whale in the midst of the sea"?

49. What did the Jaredites call the largest waters?

50. What country conquered Jerusalem after Lehi's departure?

51. What land did the people of Nephi first inhabit after separating from the Lamanites?

26. Flint (2 Ne. 5:21)

27. Seezoram's (Hel. 9:26)

28. Mosiah (Mosiah 22:13)

29. One (Alma 17:38)

30. The gentiles (2 Ne. 30:3)

31. It was to assist in the gathering of Israel and Judah

32. Amulek (Alma 10:3)

33. The army of Teancum (Alma 50:35)

34. Jacob (Jac. 6:12)

35. Two (1 Ne. 7:6)

36. Sariah, his wife (1 Ne. 5:2)

37. Manasseh (Alma 10:3)

38. King Lamoni (Alma 17:25)

39. Enos

40. He beheaded him with his own sword (1 Ne. 4:18)

41. Amulon (Mosiah 23:32)

42. The brother of Jared (Eth. 3:15)

43. Priests of Noah (Mosiah 21:23)

44. Nephi shouted to his brothers (1 Ne. 4:29–30)

45. Nephi

46. Zarahemla (Hel. 1:15)

47. His father, Alma (Mosiah 27:14)

48. The Jaredite barges (Eth. 2:24)

49. Ripliancum (Eth. 15:8)

50. Babylon (1 Ne. 1:13)

51. Nephi (Omni 1:12)

52. Where did Alma and Amulek go after leaving the city of Ammonihah?

53. Which chapter of Isaiah contains a prophecy parallel to Nephi's prophecy of the sealed book?

54. Whose servant killed Kishkumen?

55. At what city did the Nephites commit atrocities against the daughters of the Lamanites?

56. Name the six books in the Book of Mormon that re- placed the lost 116 manu- script pages.

57. Which prophet quoted in the Book of Mormon prophesied that the Lord would create a smith to bring forth an instrument for his work?

58. According to Jesus, who did his Jewish disciples think he was referring to when he spoke of his other sheep?

59. Name two of the things by which Akish swore the members of his secret combination.

60. From which Old Testament prophet did Nephi quote fifteen chapters?

61. Besides the righteous Saints, what did the people of Ammonihah burn?

62. Name four of six metals with which the Nephites worked, as listed by Jarom.

63. The "burial" of Alma the younger was compared to that of what biblical prophet?

64. The writings of which prophet did one of King Noah's priests ask Abinadi to explain?

65. Where did Ammon and the servants of King Lamoni take the king's flock to drink?

66. What prophet ended his writings with the word *adieu*?

67. Which of Pahoran's sons refused to assent to his brother's being named to the judgment seat?

68. How many gold plates did the people of Limhi find?

69. What was ziff?

70. What must a prophet possess in order to be a seer?

71. What did the people of Lehi call their last dwelling place in the Old World?

72. What was the name of the robber leader who was hung by Gidgiddoni?

73. What was the name of the river by which the family of Lehi camped three days from Jerusalem?

74. Who handed the Nephite records to Mormon?

52. Sidon (Alma 15:3)

53. Isaiah 29

54. Helaman's (Hel. 2:9)

55. Moriantum (Moro. 9:9)

56. 1 Nephi, 2 Nephi, Jacob, Enos, Jarom, Omni

57. Isaiah (3 Ne. 22:16)

58. The Gentiles (3 Ne. 15:22)

59. God, the heavens, the earth, and their heads (Eth. 8:14)

60. Isaiah

61. Scriptures (Alma 14:8)

62. Gold, silver, iron, copper, brass, and steel (Jar. 1:8)

63. Moses (Alma 45:19)

64. Isaiah (Mosiah 12:20−24)

65. The waters of Sebus (Alma 17:26)

66. Jacob (Jac. 7:27)

67. Paanchi (Hel. 1:7)

68. Twenty-four (Mosiah 8:9)

69. A metal used by the Nephites, on which they were taxed by King Noah (Mosiah 11:3, 8)

70. A seer stone or interpreter (Mosiah 8:13−17; 28:16)

71. Bountiful (1 Ne. 17:5)

72. Zemnarihah (3 Ne 4:28)

73. Laman (1 Ne. 2:8)

74. Ammaron (Morm. 1:2)

75. How did the Nephites re-cover Zarahemla in the days of Nephi and Lehi?

76. What do we learn about Ishmael's relationship to Lehi from Lucy Mack Smith's 1829 letter to her sister?

77. Who did King Mosiah cite as an example of a bad king in his discourse of why judges were preferable?

78. According to 2 Nephi 21:8 on the den of what would the weaned child someday put his hand?

79. What creatures were destroyed in the days of Jaredite King Lib?

80. "And if it so be that we are guilty, God will beat us with a few_____."

81. How did Alma and his people escape from the bondage of the Lamanites?

82. What did the three Nephites desire of Jesus that the Apostle John had also desired?

83. What five Nephite relics did the Lord promise to show to the Three Witnesses?

84. After whose temple did Nephi pattern his temple?

85. Name two Book of Mormon characters who were be-headed.

86. Who was king of the Nephites when Amaleki, the last writer on the small plates, died?

87. How did the writings of Malachi (chapters 3 and 4) come to be found in the Book of Mormon if they were written after Lehi left Jerusalem?

88. How many of the sons of Ishmael pled with Laman and Lemuel to free Nephi on the journey back to Lehi and Sariah?

89. In the days of which Nephite prophet did the people build cement homes in the land northward?

90. Who succeeded Pacumeni as chief judge?

91. To whom did Alma preach his sermon on faith?

92. The death of which Nephite was described as giving up the ghost?

93. Where did the Anti-Nephi-Lehies go following their abandonment of the Lamanite lands?

94. The people of Alma the elder were threatened with death by Noah's priests if they engaged in what activity?

95. To whom did Nephi liken the scriptures?

96. Who baptized the converts of the Samuel the Lamanite?

97. Which antichrist in the Book of Mormon was killed by supernatural means?

75. The Lamanites gave it back (Hel. 5:52)

76. Ishmael was Sariah's brother and Lehi's brother-in-law

77. King Noah (Mosiah 29:18)

78. The cockatrice

79. Poisonous serpents (Eth. 10:19)

80. Stripes (2 Ne. 28:8)

81. The Lord caused a deep sleep to come upon the Lamanites (Mosiah 24:19)

82. That they would never taste death but would live until the Second Coming (3 Ne. 28:4−8)

83. The gold plates, the sword of Laban, the breastplate, the Urim and Thummim, and the Liahona (D&C 17:1)

84. Solomon's (2 Ne. 5:16)

85. Laban (1 Ne. 4:18) and Shiz (Eth. 15:30)

86. Benjamin (Omni 1:25)

87. The Lord quoted them during his ministry to the Nephites (3 Ne. 24 and 25)

88. One (1 Ne. 7:19)

89. Helaman (Hel. 3:7)

90. Helaman (Hel. 2:2)

91. The outcasts of the Zoramites (Alma 32:2−5)

92. Sherem (Jac. 7:20)

93. Jershon (Alma 27:26)

94. Praying (Mosiah 14:11)

95. To himself and his family (1 Ne. 19:23)

96. Nephi (Hel. 16:3−4)

97. Sherem (Jac. 7:15, 21)

98. Who gave the only sermon in the Book of Mormon on plural marriage?

99. Where did Alma take his reformation movement immediately after preaching in Zarahemla?

100. Where was Ishmael buried?

101. Who was the first prophet in the Book of Mormon to mention the Lord by name?

102. According to Nephi's vision, who or what was responsible for taking away plain and precious parts from the Bible?

103. Which Book of Mormon prophet taught that the Father and the Son are one God?

104. Which Book of Mormon writer said he was not "mighty in writing like unto speaking"?

105. Who in the Book of Mormon gave the only recorded sermon on the Ten Commandments?

106. Which group in the Book of Mormon stated in their prayers that there was no Christ?

107. Why was the Brother of Jared so surprised when he saw the finger of the Lord?

108. Which three female Book of Mormon characters are specifically identified by name?

109. What was the name of Laban's servant?

110. What Jaredite leader had twenty-two children?

111. In which year after the sign of the birth of Christ did the sign of his death come?

112. Aside from corn, wheat, and barley, what other grains did the people of Zeniff raise?

113. On what mount did the brother of Jared see the finger of the Lord?

114. What did Kishkumen and the daughter of Jared have in common?

115. What New Testament sermon is also contained in the Book of Mormon?

116. What was the name of King Benjamin's second son?

117. What book in the Book of Mormon follows Omni?

118. What sin did Sherem fear he had committed?

119. Whose sons each refused to become the king of the Nephites?

120. Who was Omni's grandson?

121. Who described himself as being "over-zealous to inherit the land of our fathers"?

122. Why did Enos command Jarom to write on the plates?

123. Who prayed from his garden tower?

98. Jacob (Jac. 2:23−35)

99. Gideon (Alma 6:8)

100. Nahum (1 Ne. 16:34)

101. Jacob (2 Ne. 10:3)

102. The great and abominable church (1 Ne. 13:26)

103. Abinadi (Mosiah 15:4)

104. Nephi (2 Ne. 33:1)

105. Abinadi (Mosiah 12 and 13)

106. The Zoramites (Alma 31:16)

107. He "knew not that the Lord had flesh and blood" (Eth. 3:8)

108. Sariah (1 Ne. 2:5), Abish (Alma 19:16), and Isabel (Alma 39:3)

109. Zoram (1 Ne. 4:35)

110. The brother of Jared (Eth. 6:20)

111. The thirty-fourth (3 Ne. 8:5)

112. Neas and sheum (Mosiah 9:9)

113. Shelem (Eth. 3:1)

114. Each was instrumental in founding a secret combination (Hel. 1:11; Eth. 8:8−9)

115. The Sermon on the Mount (3 Ne. 12−14)

116. Helorum (Mosiah 1:2)

117. Words of Mormon

118. The unpardonable sin (Jac. 7:19)

119. Mosiah (Mosiah 29:3)

120. Abinadom (Omni 1:10)

121. Zeniff (Mosiah 9:3)

122. That their genealogy might kept (Jar. 1:1)

123. Nephi (Hel. 7:10)

124. Gidgiddoni and Giddianhi were opponents. Which was the righteous commander and which was the robber chief?

125. What land was between the land of Zarahemla and the land of Nephi?

126. What did the king's servants present to Lamoni as evidence that Ammon had cut off the arms of the Lamanites?

127. What two Nephite leaders captured the city of Manti, under Helaman's direction?

128. To whom did Alma state that "wickedness never was happiness"?

129. What two Nephite prophets disappeared without explanation?

130. Which of Ishmael's daughters did Zoram marry?

131. According to 2 Nephi 24:12−14, who aspired to ascend to heaven and to be like the Most High?

132. What languages did Charles Anthon say the untranslated characters shown to him by Martin Harris were?

133. In what valley did Alma camp following his initial victory over the Amlicites?

134. What Jaredite king "did justice unto his people" but not to himself?

135. By what power do angels speak?

136. What is the subtitle printed on the cover of all new softbound editions of the Book of Mormon?

137. According to anti-Mormons, what book by Ethan Smith was used by Joseph Smith in writing the Book of Mormon?

138. Who provided the punctuation for the first edition of the Book of Mormon?

139. Toward what Nephite land did the Jaredite flocks flee from the poisonous serpents?

140. What mark did the Amlicites put on their bodies?

141. Who were to be a scourge to the seed of Nephi?

142. How many mighty men had died before Coriantumr began to repent of his evil?

143. Who was the chief among the four sons of Mosiah?

144. What biblical prophet was Nephi paraphrasing when he said that God reveals line upon line and precept upon precept?

145. "But the laborer in Zion shall labor for Zion; for if they labor for_____they shall perish."

146. Who commanded Jacob to write on the small plates of Nephi?

147. What book precedes the book of Alma in the Book of Mormon?

124. Gidgiddoni was righteous; Giddianhi was the robber (3 Ne. 3)

125. Minon (Alma 2:24)

126. The arms (Alma 17:39)

127. Gid and Teomner (Alma 58:16)

128. Corianton (Alma 41:10)

129. Alma the younger; and Nephi, son of Helaman (Alma 46:18; 3 Ne. 1:3)

130. The eldest (1 Ne. 16:7)

131. Lucifer

132. Egyptian, Chaldaic, Assyriac, and Arabic (JS-H 1:64)

133. Gideon (Alma 2:20)

134. Morianton (Eth. 10:11)

135. By the Holy Ghost (2 Ne. 32:3)

136. Another Testament of Jesus Christ

137. *View of the Hebrews*

138. The printer, E. B. Grandin

139. Zarahemla (Eth. 9:31)

140. A red mark on their foreheads (Alma 3:3)

141. The Lamanites (2 Ne. 5:25)

142. Two million (Eth. 15:2)

143. Ammon (Alma 17:18)

144. Isaiah (2 Ne. 28:30; Isa. 28:13)

145. Money (2 Ne. 26:31)

146. Nephi (Jac. 1:2)

147. Mosiah

148. Which Book of Mormon writer prophesied that his readers would meet him "face to face" before the bar of God?

149. At what rate were King Noah's people taxed by the Lamanites?

150. What two Book of Mormon prophets identified the mother of Jesus by name?

151. When Nephi said, "I will go and do the things which the Lord hath commanded" what had the Lord just commanded?

152. Name one writer in the book of Omni other than Omni.

153. How many chapters of Isaiah does Nephi quote in their entirety in First Nephi?

154. Who preached to his people from a specially constructed tower?

155. Who persuaded the brother of Jared to permit the Jaredites to have a king?

156. What was heaped upon the land as dung in the days of Mormon?

157. Where did the priests of King Noah live after they were expelled from the land of Nephi?

158. What was the name of the valley where the Jaredites camped after leaving Babel?

159. In what hill did Ammaron hide the Nephite records?

160. What people found Coriantumr, the last king of the Jaredites?

161. Why was the book of Daniel not contained in the brass plates?

162. Why did Lehi and his family eat raw meat while in the wilderness after leaving Jerusalem?

163. What Lamanite general captured Zarahemla and killed chief judge Pacumeni?

164. What two books of the Book of Mormon are out of chronological order?

165. Name one of the three Book of Mormon prophets who refers to the victory of the grave and the sting of death.

166. What was the name of the valley where Alma the elder's people camped after escaping the Lamanites?

167. To whom did Mormon write his epistle regarding infant baptism?

168. Jesus commanded the Nephites to record prophecies that had not yet been written. Whose prophecies were they?

169. Of what kind of workmanship was the Liahona?

170. Who is the only Lamanite prophet in the Book of Mormon identified by name?

148. Nephi (2 Ne. 33:11)

149. 20 percent (one-fifth)
     (Mosiah 11:3)

150. Benjamin (Mosiah 3:8) and
     Alma (7:10)

151. To get the brass plates from
     Laban (1 Ne. 3:2−4)

152. Chemish, Amaron,
     Abinadom, Amaleki

153. Two−Isaiah 48 and 49
     (1 Ne. 20 and 21)

154. King Benjamin (Mosiah 2:7)

155. Jared (Eth. 6:24)

156. The dead Nephites (Morm.
     2:15)

157. Amulon (Mosiah 23:31)

158. Moriancumer (Eth. 2:13)

159. Shim (Morm. 4:23)

160. The Mulekites (Omni 1:21)

161. It was written after Lehi
     left Jerusalem

162. The Lord commanded them
     not to make fire (1 Ne.
     17:2, 12)

163. Coriantumr (Hel. 1:21)

164. Words of Mormon, Ether

165. Abinadi (Mosiah 16:8),
     Aaron (Alma 22:14), and
     Mormon (Morm. 7:5)

166. Alma (Mosiah 24:20)

167. Moroni (Moro. 8:1)

168. Samuel the Lamanite's
     (3 Ne. 23:11−13)

169. Curious (1 Ne. 16:10)

170. Samuel the Lamanite (Hel.
     13:2)

171. What does the Book of Mormon tell us is meant by the statement that Moses was "buried by the hand of the Lord"?

172. Who was Alma baptizing when Alma also immersed himself?

173. What was the name of the stand on which the Zoramites stood to pray?

174. Who did the king of the Lamanites make ruler over Alma and his people in the city of Helam?

175. Who did King Tubaloth of the Lamanites appoint as general?

176. To what land did Ammon first go on his mission to the Lamanites?

177. According to 2 Nephi 17:14, who would conceive and bear a son?

178. According to Martin Harris, Charles Anthon said, "I cannot read a _____ book."

179. What book of the Book of Mormon follows the book of Omni?

180. What chapter is known as the Psalm of Nephi?

181. According to the prophecy of Joseph, as related by Lehi, what was to be the name of the great seer?

182. How many people do we have record of having seen the gold plates in this dispensation?

183. Who killed Amalickiah?

184. Who was the first king of the Jaredites?

185. Why did Jacob say the Lamanites were more righteous than the Nephites?

186. Jesus quoted all of Isaiah chapter 54 to the Nephites. What prophet quoted all of chapter 53?

187. What group of people was the Lamanite army chasing when it discovered the people of Alma?

188. With whom had Laban been meeting the night he was killed by Nephi?

189. What did the sons of Mosiah and the sons of the brother of Jared have in common?

190. Who said, "I speak unto you as if ye were present, and yet ye are not"?

191. In quoting Isaiah 48:1, Nephi parenthetically tells us what the Waters of Judah are. What are they?

192. Who was king of Jerusalem when Lehi left Jerusalem?

193. On what hill did the Amlicites make war on the Nephites?

194. According to the new edition of the Book of Mormon, what was the year of Christ's birth?

195. What did the iron rod represent?

171. He was taken up by the Spirit, or translated (Alma 45:19)

172. Helam (Mosiah 18:14)

173. Rameumpton (Alma 31:13–14,21)

174. Amulon (Mosiah 23:39)

175. Coriantumr (Hel. 1:16)

176. Ishmael (Alma 17:9)

177. A virgin

178. Sealed (JS-H 1:65)

179. Words of Mormon

180. 2 Nephi 4

181. Joseph (2 Ne. 3:15)

182. Twelve (Joseph Smith, the the Three Witnesses, and the Eight Witnesses)

183. Teancum (Alma 52:34)

184. Onihah (Eth. 6:27)

185. Their husbands had only one wife and no concubines (Jac. 3:5–7)

186. Abinadi (Mosiah 14)

187. The people of King Limhi (Mosiah 22:14–16)

188. The elders of the Jews (1 Ne. 4:22)

189. They all refused the kingship (Eth. 6:25; Mosiah 29:3)

190. Mormon (Morm. 8:35)

191. The waters of baptism (2 Ne. 20:1)

192. Zedekiah (1 Ne. 1:4)

193. Amnihu (Alma 2:15)

194. A.D. 1

195. The word of God (1 Ne. 15:23–24)

196. Which recordkeeper admitted that he was a wicked man who had not kept the commandments as he should have?

197. Who first possessed the land of Ammonihah?

198. What two Book of Mormon prophets prophesied of churches built up in the last days for gain?

199. In what land were Alma and his people dwelling when they were discovered by the Lamanites?

200. Who pled for Abinadi's life after King Noah commanded his death?

201. To what was Oliver Cowdery referring when he said, "These were days never to be forgotten"?

202. What did Alma the younger and Nephi son of Helaman have in common with Dallin Oaks?

203. Name one of the four spies sent by Alma to watch over the camp of the Amlicites.

204. To what were Mosiah's seer stones, or interpreters, fastened?

205. According to Nephi, the devil will pacify and "lull the wicked into _____ security."

206. Of whom was Mormon a pure descendant?

207. How did Limhi's people escape from the captivity of the Lamanites?

208. Who authored the most chapters in the Book of Mormon?

209. How did Limhi describe to Ammon the land where the twenty four gold plates were discovered?

210. Who prevented Laman and Lemuel from beating Nephi in the cave outside of Jerusalem?

211. What did Amulek answer when Zeezrom asked if there was more than one god?

212. What Book of Mormon author with a book named after him has the most letters in his name?

213. According to King Limhi, what is greater than a prophet?

214. What is inaccurate about Arnold Friberg's painting of Alma baptizing at the waters of Mormon?

215. What two groups of Nephites in the Book of Mosiah were subjected to bondage by the Lamanites?

216. Who was the last Nephite chief judge?

217. In support of whom did Kishkumen commit his first recorded murder?

196. Omni (Omni 1:2)

197. Ammonihah (Alma 8:7)

198. Nephi (2 Ne. 28:3, 12–13), and Mormon (Morm. 8:32–33)

199. Helam (Mosiah 23:20)

200. Alma (Mosiah 17:2)

201. The translation of the Book of Mormon (J—H 1:71 footnote)

202. All were judges before taking up the ministry full time

203. Zeram, Amnor, Manti, and Limher (Alma 2:22)

204. The two rims of a bow (Mosiah 28:13)

205. Carnal (2 Ne. 28:21)

206. Lehi (3 Ne. 5:20)

207. They gave wine to the Lamanite guards and escaped while they were drunk (Mosiah 22:3–10)

208. Mormon

209. A land covered with the bones of men and beasts and the ruins of buildings (Mosiah 8:8)

210. An Angel (1 Ne. 3:29)

211. No (Alma 11:29)

212. Helaman

213. A seer (Mosiah 8:15)

214. The trees near the water were small (Mosiah 18:5)

215. The people of Limhi (Mosiah 21:13) and the people of Alma (Mosiah 24)

216. Lachoneus (3 Ne. 6:19; 7:1)

217. Paanchi (Hel. 1:7–9)

218. What biblical prophet was preaching in Jerusalem at the time of Lehi?

219. How many writers contributed to the book of Omni?

220. Who was Nephi's guide when he received his vision of the tree of life?

221. In what language did Nephi write the small plates?

222. Who led the band of Kishkumen?

223. Which judge was murdered by "an unknown hand"?

224. Who was a man of "no small reputation" among the people of Ammonihah?

225. What river ran by the land of Zarahemla?

226. Who was king over the land of Ishmael?

227. What chapter of Isaiah did Abinadi quote to King Noah?

228. What did Zeezrom have in common with Oliver Cowdery, Marion G. Romney, and Bruce R. McConkie?

229. On which hill was Nehor executed?

230. Who described the Nephites as "a lonesome and solemn people, wanderers, cast out from Jerusalem"?

231. Why did Amaleki deliver the small plates to King Benjamin?

232. Who is the only Book of Mormon person, mentioned by name, to have been raised from the dead?

233. Who did Abinadi say were the seed of Christ referred to in Isaiah 53:10?

234. Ammon told King Limhi that what person could translate the twenty-four gold plates?

235. In place of sacrifices of burnt offerings, what did Jesus command the Nephites to sacrifice?

236. Which prophecy concerning the last days is repeated more frequently than any other in the Book of Mormon?

237. With which Nephite general did Coriantumr fight?

238. The Book of Mormon was written to convince whom that Jesus is the Christ?

239. According to Jesus, over what doctrine had there been disputes and contention among the Nephites prior to his visitation?

240. According to King Benjamin, the Nephites were not to suffer beggars to put up their petitions in what way?

241. According to King Mosiah, what will the majority of the people always desire?

218. Jeremiah (1 Ne. 7:14)

219. Five

220. The Spirit of the Lord (1 Ne. 11:11)

221. The language of the Egyptians (1 Ne. 1:2)

222. Gadianton (Hel. 2:4)

223. Cezoram (Hel. 6:15)

224. Amulek (Alma 10:4)

225. Sidon (Alma 2:15)

226. Lamoni (Alma 17:21)

227. Isaiah 53 (Mosiah 14)

228. All were lawyers by profession

229. The hill Manti (Alma 1:15)

230. Jacob (Jac. 7:26)

231. Amaleki had no son (Omni 1:25)

232. Timothy, brother of Nephi (3 Ne. 19:4)

233. All those who have faith in Christ (Mosiah 15:10–13)

234. King Mosiah (Mosiah 8:14)

235. A broken heart and contrite spirit (3 Ne. 9:19–20)

236. Gathering of Israel

237. Moronihah

238. The Jew and the Gentile (Title page)

239. Baptism (3 Ne. 11:22, 28)

240. In vain (Mosiah 4:16)

241. That which is right (Mosiah 29:26)

242. What did Alma do after King Mosiah refused to judge transgressors in the Church?

243. In what activity were the daughters of the Lamanites engaged when they were captured by Noah's priests?

244. What other prophet said, as Nephi did in 2 Nephi 4:17, "O wretched man that I am"?

245. Who baptized King Limhi and his people?

246. With what were the Lamanites who captures Nephi and Lehi encircled?

247. Who did Nephi foresee would take plain and precious things out of the Bible?

248. Where did Alma take his reform movement immediatcly prior to going to Ammonihah?

249. Why didn't Mormon write the names of the Three Nephites?

250. What did the people of Lehi call the sea?

251. To what land did Mosiah lead his people?

252. What was the name of the campsite of Lehi's family four days south of the valley of Lemuel?

253. From whom was the Ammon descended who met King Limhi?

254. How many of the twelve Nephite disciples had Bible names?

255. In the days of Giddianhi, the robber, who was chief judge of the Nephites?

256. What two lands was Limhi the king of?

257. For what were Limhi's men searching when they discovered the land covered with dry bones?

258. According to Captain Moroni, what happened to Joseph's coat of many colors after it was brought back to his father?

259. What gift did both King Mosiahs have?

260. What did the children of Noah's priests do to show their displeasure with the conduct of their fathers?

261. What relative of Joseph Smith also had a dream of the tree of life?

262. Whose order of priestcraft did the people of Ammonihah follow?

263. Who preached among the people of King Noah in disguise?

242. Prayed and received a revelation that transgressors who refused to repent would be cut off from the Church (Mosiah 26:15–16)

243. Singing, dancing, and making merry (Mosiah 20:1)

244. Paul (Rom. 7:24)

245. Alma (Mosiah 25:18)

246. Fire (Hel. 5:44)

247. The great and abominable church (1 Ne. 13:26, 28)

248. Melek (Alma 8:6)

249. The Lord forbade him (3 Ne. 28:25)

250. Irreantum (1 Ne. 17:1)

251. Zarahemla (Omni 1:4)

252. Shazer (1 Ne. 16:13)

253. Zarahemla (Mosiah 7:3)

254. Six — Timothy, Jonas, Jeremiah, Jonas, Zedekiah, and Isaiah (3 Ne. 19:4)

255. Lachoneus (3 Ne. 3)

256. Nephi and Shilom (Mosiah 7:7)

257. Zarahemla (Mosiah 21:26)

258. A remnant was preserved without decay (Alma 46:24)

259. The gift of translation (Omni 1:20–21; Mosiah 28:13–17)

260. Renounced their fathers' names and took upon them the name of Nephi (Mosiah 25:12)

261. His father

262. Nehor's (Alma 15:15)

263. Abinadi (Mosiah 12:1)

264. In what language were the brass plates written?

265. Name all of the things the Angel Moroni statue on the top of the Salt Lake Temple holds in his hands.

266. What did Lehi name the valley in which he and his family camped by the Red Sea?

267. What did Nephi notice about the river of water in his vision of the tree of life that Lehi did not observe?

268. Who abridged the book of Ether?

269. According to 1 Nephi 14:10, what are the two churches to which everyone belongs?

270. What Nephite land was near the Jaredite land of Moron?

271. What was the place named where Alma the elder first baptized?

272. What was the name of King Bejamin's third son?

273. In the days of King Mosiah, which were *least* numerous, the Nephites, the Lamanites, or the people of Zarahemla?

274. In the days of King Lib, what area of the land was preserved by the Jaredites as a wilderness to get game?

275. How many men could Laban command?

276. What or who did Lamoni initially think Ammon to be?

277. Whose prophecy was fulfilled when King Noah was burned by his own priests?

278. What was the pattern Nephi used in making swords for his people?

279. What happened to Mormon's abridgment of the record from Lehi down to the reign of King Benjamin?

280. From what did Mosiah translate the account of Coriantumr, the last of the Jaredites?

281. To whom did the devil appear as an angel?

282. How did the Nephites to whom Benjamin gave his discourse know that they had received a remission of sins?

283. For what were the large plates of Nephi used?

284. What did Amulek answer when Zeezrom asked him if the Son of God was the very Eternal Father?

285. Who was king of the Nephites when the merged with the people of Zarahemla?

286. What Jaredite prophet observed the destruction of his people?

287. In what land did the daughters of the Lamanites gather to sing, dance and make merry?

264. The language of the Egyptians (Mosiah 1:4)

265. His horn

266. Lemuel (1 Ne. 2:14)

267. The water was filthy (1 Ne. 15:26)

268. Moroni (Eth. 1:1)

269. The Church of the Lamb of God or the Church of the Devil

270. Desolation (Eth. 7:15)

271. The Waters of Mormon (Mosiah 18:8)

272. Helaman (Mosiah 1:2)

273. Nephites (Mosiah 25:2—3)

274. The land south (Eth. 10:21)

275. Fifty (1 Ne. 3:31)

276. The Great Spirit (Alma 18:2)

277. Abinadi's (Mosiah 12:3)

278. The sword of Laban (2 Ne. 5:14)

279. It was lost with the 116 manuscript pages

280. A large stone (Omni 1:20—21)

281. Korihor (Alma 30:53)

282. They were filled with joy and had peace of conscience (Mosiah 4:3)

283. Keeping the history of the secular dealings of the Nephites (1 Ne. 9:2, 4)

284. Yes (Alma 11:39)

285. Mosiah (Omni 1:12—14)

286. Ether (Eth. 15:33)

287. In Shemlon (Mosiah 20:1)

288. Name three persons in the Book of Mormon who gave commands to search the prophecies of Isaiah.

289. From what did Akish learn of the plans of the secret combination of ancient days?

290. Who did Coriantumr kill at the walls of Zarahemla?

291. In what languages was Nephi taught?

292. Who are the only two women named in the Book of Mormon who were characters in the Bible?

293. What Nephite missionary was described as "wise yet harmless"?

294. Which Nephite had the same first name as the founder of the Republic of Texas?

295. Who said, "Adam fell that men might be; and men are, that they might have joy"?

296. What did Lehi read about in the book given to him by the heavenly messenger in 1 Nephi 1?

297. From whom did Mormon learn of Lamanite atrocities at Sherrizah?

298. According to Nephi, what would the sealed book spoken of by Isaiah contain?

299. To whom was the Lord referring when he said, "It is better that one man should perish . . ."?

300. Whose letter does Moroni quote on the subject of infant baptism?

Simpler Questions for Use as Needed

301. Name one of the two things that caused great destructions in the Nephite lands after the Lord was crucified.

302. Who in the Book of Mormon "clapped their hands for joy" when they were challenged to be baptized?

303. Who was the first prophet of the Jaredites—Jared, the brother of Jared, Ether, or Shiz?

304. Who built the ship that took the Nephites across the ocean to the promised land?

305. How did Alma and Amulek escape from prison? Did an earthquake break down the walls, did they bribe the guards, or did they did a tunnel?

306. Why did Samuel the Lamanite preach from the walls of the city?

288. Nephi (2 Ne. 11:2), Jesus (3 Ne. 23:1), and Mormon (Morm. 8:23)

289. The records that were brought across the deep by the Jaredites (Eth. 8:9)

290. Pacumeni (Hel. 1:21)

291. The languages of the Jews and of the Egyptians (1 Ne. 1:2)

292. Eve and Mary

293. Ammon (Alma 18:22)

294. Sam, son of Lehi (Sam Houston)

295. Lehi (2 Ne. 2:25)

296. The destruction of Jerusalem and the coming of the Messiah (1 Ne. 1:13, 19)

297. Amoron (Moro. 9:7)

298. A revelation from God from the beginning of the world to the end (2 Ne. 27:7)

299. Laban (1 Ne. 4:13)

300. Mormon's (Moro. 8:1, 8, 9)

301. A terrible storm and a great earthquake (3 Ne. 8:12)

302. The people of Lehi-Nephi to whom Alma preached at the Waters of Mormon (Mosiah 18:11)

303. The brother of Jared

304. Nephi (1 Ne. 18:1–4)

305. An earthquake broke down the walls (Alma 14:27)

306. The people wouldn't let him into the city (Hel. 13:4)

307. How old was Mormon when he "was visited of the Lord" — ten, fifteen, twenty, or thirty?

308. How many books of Nephi are in the Book of Mormon —two, three, four or five?

309. Nephi, son of Helaman, asked the Lord to do something to the Nephites to help them repent. Did he ask for diseases, a war, famine, or and earthquake?

310. After Joseph Smith translated the Book of Mormon, how many people did an angel show the gold plates to?

311. How many different records did Nephi keep — two, three, or four?

312. Where did Alma the younger and the three sons of Mosiah go after they repented of their wickedness?

313. When the Nephites first wore thick clothing and armor to fight the Lamanites, what did the Lamanites wear?

314. Jesus gave three of his Nephite disciples a special blessing. What was it?

315. Who was the last prophet of the Nephites — Mormon, Moroni, Nephi, or Ether?

316. Who translated the Book of Mormon?

317. What weapon did Nephi use to kill Laban?

318. What prophet was very wicked as a young man, then repented and changed his life?

319. How many times each week would the wicked Zoramites pray?

320. When the Lord visited America, he taught the people a sermon he had also given in Palestine. What is the name of the sermon?

321. Where did Ether hide while his people were at war — in his house, by the seashore, in the forest, or in a cave?

322. What Old Testament prophet did the Lord quote most when he visited America — Ezekiel, Isaiah, Malachi, or Daniel?

323. Who was Nephi's mother — Ruth, Deborah, Sariah, or Phoebe?

324. What good king in the Book of Mormon built a tower to teach his people — Helaman, Mosiah, Benjamin, or Nephi?

325. What did the people of Anti-Nephi-Lehi do to protect themselves when the Lamanites attacked — sharpened their swords, built forts, or prayed?

326. Samuel the Lamanite preached that a sign would be given to show that the Lord had been crucified. What was the sign?

307. Fifteen (Morm. 1:15)

308. Four

309. Famine (Hel. 11:4)

310. Three (the Three Witnesses)

311. Two, a Church history and a regular history (1 Ne. 9:4)

312. On missions (Mosiah 27:35—37)

313. Nothing—they were nearly naked (Alma 43:19—20)

314. That they would never die (3 Ne. 28:7—8)

315. Moroni

316. Joseph Smith

317. Laban's sword (1 Ne. 4:18)

318. Alma the younger (Mosiah 27:8, 28)

319. Once (Alma 31:12, 23)

320. The Sermon on the Mount (3 Ne. 12—14)

321. In a cave (Eth. 13:14)

322. Isaiah

323. Sariah (1 Ne. 2:5)

324. Benjamin (Mosiah 2:7)

325. They prayed (Alma 24:21)

326. Three days of total darkness throughout the land (3 Ne. 8:3)

327. What did the Lord touch with his finger to give the Jaredites lights for their boats?

328. How many people did the Lord tell Joseph Smith he could show the gold plates to—three, five, eight, or eleven?

329. What was the special compass the Lord gave the Nephites to help them journey through the wilderness?

330. When robbers attacked the flocks of a Lamanite king, Ammon cut off their arms. What did his companions do with the arms?

331. Samuel the Lamanite preached that a sign would be given to show that the Lord had been born. What was the sign?

332. Who was the general of the Nephite armies in their last great battle—Teancum, Mormon, Moroni, or Ether?

333. What does the book of Ether talk about most—prophecies, gospel teachings, war, or the Church?

334. When Nephi, son of Helaman, was preaching, he said someone had just been murdered. Was it a priest, a prophet, a soldier, or a chief judge?

335. Who were Nephi's three older brothers?

336. What great prophet was converted by the prophet Abinadi—Helaman, Alma, Timothy, or Ammon?

337. Who told Amulek that Alma the younger was a prophet—Alma the leder, Zeezrom, Mosiah, or an angel?

338. What great general led the Nephites in their wars against the Lamanites in the last part of the book of Alma—Teancum, Moroni, or Corom?

339. Name one of the two things that enriched the little children after Jesus blessed them.

340. Who was the last prophet of the Jaredites—Shiz, Coriantumr, Ether, or Jared?

341. Who told Joseph Smith where he could find the gold plates?

342. How did Nephi trick Laban's servant into thinking that Nephi was Laban?

343. When Ammon was a servant to the Lamanite king, was he also a soldier, spy, or a missionary?

344. Who built ships to explore the lands to the north—Hagoth, Shiblon, Pahoran, or Zoram?

345. How old was Mormon when Ammaron chose him to to keep the history of the Nephites—ten, fifteen, thirty, or fifty-five?

327. Stones (Eth. 3:6)

328. Eight (the Eight Witnesses—an angel showed the plates to the Three Witnesses)

329. The Liahona (Alma 37:38)

330. Took them to the king (Alma 17:39)

331. A day and a night and a day without any darkness at all (Hel. 14:3—4)

332. Mormon (Morm. 5:1)

333. War

334. Chief judge (Hel. 8:27)

335. Laman, Lemuel, and Sam (1 Ne. 2:5)

336. Alma (Mosiah 17:2)

337. An angel (Alma 8:20)

338. Moroni (not the same as the angel Moroni)

339. Angels and fire (3 Ne. 17:24)

340. Ether

341. The angel Moroni

342. Nephi put on Laban's clothes (1 Ne. 4:21)

343. A missionary (Alma 17:25)

344. Hagoth (Alma 63:5)

345. Ten (Morm. 1:2)

346. How many separate books
     are in the Book of
     Mormon — nine, twelve,
     fifteen, or eighteen?

347. What prophet was burned
     to death for his testimony —
     Abinadi, Lehi, Ammoron, or
     Riplah?

348. Who was Nephi's father?

349. What wicked king in the
     Book of Mormon had the
     same name as a prophet in
     the Bible?

350. Where would the Zoramites
     stand when they prayed out
     loud to God — in the street,
     in the church, on a hill, or
     on their roofs?

346. Fifteen

347. Abinadi (Mosiah 17:20)

348. Lehi (1 Ne. 1:5)

349. King Noah (Mosiah 11:1–2)

350. In the church, on a tall
     stand (Alma 31:13)

PART 4 Church History

1. By whose instruction was Joseph Smith called the "first elder of the Church"?

2. In the early days of the Church, what did priesthood holders carry with them as evidence of authority to perform the duties of their callings?

3. Who was ordained an elder immediately after Oliver Cowdery, the "second elder of the Church," was ordained?

4. In what year were more of the sections in the Doctrine and Covenants received than in any other year?

5. More than thirteen hundred men endured imprisonment for what principle of the gospel?

6. Three of our Church Presidents have had the same first and last name. What was it?

7. Who was the only President of the Church besides Joseph Smith not previously sustained as President of the Quorum of the Twelve?

8. Hyrum Smith read extracts from the works of what historian less than two hours before the martyrdom?

9. What was the name given to the group of Mormon men who marched from Kirtland, Ohio, to Jackson County to aid their besieged brethren?

10. In what publication were parts of the Book of Mormon printed without permission two months before copies of the book itself were available?

11. What geographical area became known as "the granary" of the Great Basin kingdom?

12. For what purpose did the Lord want President Snow to go to St. George in the spring of 1899?

13. When Johnston's Army set up camp in Cedar Valley what did they name their encampment?

14. How many people were included in the Church's organizing charter?

15. When the Mormon pioneers first applied for statehood, what did they call their state?

16. At the turn or the twentieth century, approximately how many members of the Church were there — 153,000; 198,000; 215,000; or 268,000?

17. What collection of theological lessons was originally published with the Doctrine and Covenants but was omitted in 1921?

18. How many men belonged to the Mormon Battalion?

19. What famous couplet did Lorenzo Snow write after receiving a revelation?

1. John the Baptist's (*HC*, 1:40—41)

2. Licenses (D&C 20:63—64)

3. Joseph Smith, the "first elder of the Church" (*HC*, 1:77—78; D&C 20:2—3)

4. In 1831 (thirty-seven revelations)

5. Plural marriage (*CHC*, 6:222)

6. Joseph Smith (Joseph Smith, Joseph F. Smith, Joseph Fielding Smith)

7. Joseph F. Smith (*ABM*, p. 300)

8. Josephus (*HC*, 6:615)

9. Zion's Camp (*OHUM*, p. 31)

10. The *Palmyra Reflector*, a satirical paper distributed locally (*EN*, 12/83, p. 51)

11. The Bear Lake Valley (*OHUM*, p. 72)

12. To urge the Church to live the law of tithing (*ETN*, p. 455)

13. Camp Floyd (*OHUM*, p. 92)

14. Six (*HC*, 1:76)

15. Deseret (*OHUM*, p. 80)

16. 268,000 (*ETN*, p. 459)

17. The Lectures on Faith

18. Five hundred (*OHUM*, p. 49)

19. "As man now is, God once was; As God is, man may become" (*ETN*, p. 441)

20. Martin Harris took a copy of some characters from the Book of Mormon plates to New York City to be examined by whom?

21. In 1828 the Prophet Joseph Smith lost the privilege of translating the Book of Mormon for a time. Why?

22. What initially served as the judicial system in Utah?

23. Within one thousand, how many members of the Church were excommunicated in England in the years 1851 through 1855?

24. What is the JST?

25. Who was the "second elder of the Church"?

26. What was the first of all the the Mormon periodicals?

27. Which President of the Church recorded that he was involved in twenty-seven serious accidents during his lifetime?

28. Who did the Lord refer to in the Doctrine and Covenants as "an elect lady"?

29. Utah's first batch of alfalfa seed came from what country?

30. Which of the Three Witnesses ultimately denied his testimony of the Book of Mormon?

31. How many stories tall does the Kirtland Temple stand?

32. What instrument did Moroni give Joseph Smith for translating the Book of Mormon?

33. How did the Church respond to John C. Bennett's vicious attacks?

34. Within one thousand troops, how large did the Nauvoo Legion grow?

35. Who was the first President of the Church since Joseph Smith *not* to wear a beard?

36. Who was instructed to make the first selection of hymns for the Church?

37. Which group of witnesses to the Book of Mormon were permitted to actually handle the gold plates?

38. What did Utah ironworkers do with cannonballs brought into Utah by the invading U.S. army?

39. In 1906, the Relief Society donated wheat it had stored to whom?

40. What was the Prophet Joseph Smith's last recorded prophecy?

41. What monument was dedicated at the first Pioneer Day celebration in 1897?

42. What natural barrier served as the western boundary for the state of Deseret?

20. Professor Charles Anthon (JS-H 1:64)

21. Because of the loss of the first 116 pages of the Book of Mormon translation (D&C 10:1–2)

22. Church courts (*OHUM*, p. 79)

23. Fifteen thousand (*OHUM*, pp. 99–100)

24. The Joseph Smith Translation of the Bible

25. Oliver Cowdery (D&C 20:3, JS-H 1:72)

26. *The Evening and the Morning Star* (*ME*, p. 207)

27. Wilford Woodruff (*ABM*, p. 396)

28. Emma Smith (D&C 25:3)

29. Australia (*OHUM*, p. 64)

30. None of them

31. Two (*OHUM*, p. 27)

32. The Urim and Thummim (JS-H 1:59)

33. It sent out more missionaries to teach people the truth (*OHUM*, p. 41)

34. Five thousand (*OHUM*, p. 39)

35. David O. McKay (*ABM*, p. 189)

36. Emma Smith (D&C 25:11)

37. The Eight Witnesses (*HC*, 1:58)

38. They transformed them into mill rollers and other useful articles (*OHUM*, p. 67)

39. Earthquake victims in San Francisco (*ME*, p. 233)

40. He prophesied that Dan Jones would live to fulfill a mission to Wales (*HC*, 6:601)

41. The Brigham Young Monument (*ETN*, p. 436)

42. The Sierra Nevada Mountains (*OHUM*, p. 80)

43. Why did President Snow ask Church members to purchase $1,500,000 worth of bonds in 1898?

44. What was the very first commandment given to the newly organized Church?

45. The Mormons paid Miles Goodyear $1950 for his Utah ranch in 1848. What was the property worth in 1850?

46. What was the main business of the territorial legislature on December 18, 1856?

47. What four things were early missionaries instructed not to take with them on their missions?

48. What governmental body destroyed the anti-Mormon *Nauvoo Expositor* in 1844?

49. On January 27, 1878, the first western stake outside of Utah was organized. What southwestern state was it located in?

50. On June 11, 1829, Joseph Smith went to Palmyra to obtain what from the U.S. District Court?

51. When an entire ship's crew was converted by emigrating Mormons, how were the men baptized?

52. At the Jubilee Conference on April 6, 1880, what debt owed to the Church was cut in half?

53. How long was it between the time when the Salt Lake Temple capstone was set in place and the day the temple was dedicated?

54. Who was the first chief justice of the state of Deseret?

55. Why did ship's captains complain that Mormon emigrants made their ships lay an inch lower in the water?

56. How many stakes comprised the Church in the spring of 1899 — twenty, thirty, forty, or fifty?

57. What nickname was given to the route between Lakes Erie and Ontario in the early days of the Church, because of missionary and convert traffic?

58. Who paid the printing costs for the first edition of the Book of Mormon?

59. Which section of the Doctrine and Covenants is known as the "Revelation on Church Organization and Government" or Constitution of the Church"?

60. Who was told by Joseph Smith, "Cut not thy hair and no bullet or blade can harm thee"?

61. How many General Authorities have had the first name *Brigham*?

43. To help the Church get out debt (*ETN*, p. 454)

44. "There shall be a record [a history] kept among you" (D&C 22:1)

45. Nearly a million dollars (*OHUM*, p. 60)

46. Heber C. Kimball preached to and rebaptized the legislators (*OHUM*, p. 87)

47. "No purse nor scrip, neither staves [meaning "staffs"], neither two coats" (D&C 24:18)

48. The Nauvoo city council (*OHUM*, p. 44)

49. Arizona (*ETN*, p. 407)

50. The copyright for the Book of Mormon (*EN*, 12/83, p. 40)

51. In a large water barrel placed on deck and filled with sea water (*OHUM*, p. 103)

52. The Perpetual Emigration Fund (*ETN*, p. 409)

53. Exactly one year (April 6, 1892 to April 6, 1893) *ETN*, p. 432)

54. Heber C. Kimball (*OHUM*, p. 81)

55. Because emigrating Mormon craftsmen brought so many heavy tools (*OHUM*, p. 102)

56. Forty (*ETN*, p. 455)

57. The Mormon Road (*OHUM*, pp. 25—26)

58. Martin Harris

59. Section 20

60. Orrin Porter Rockwell (*ABM*, p. 251)

61. Three—Brigham Young; Brigham Young, Jr.; B. H. Roberts (*MMZ*, p. 528)

62. Which section of the Doctrine and Covenants was received earliest?

63. How many copies of the Book of Mormon were printed in the first edition?

64. Who promised Joseph Smith and Oliver Cowdery that they would receive the Melchizedek Priesthood in due time?

65. The silkworms that were to be raised in Utah came from what European country?

66. What was the name of the city militia provided for in the Nauvoo Charter?

67. Who organized the Council of Fifty, designed partly to prepare a government for the Lord's Second Coming?

68. What intermountain state was subject to much colonization during the period 1877–1880—Colorado, Wyoming, Arizona, or New Mexico?

69. Who was Church President when the Salt Lake Temple was completed and dedicated?

70. All but how many of the sections of the Doctrine and Covenants were received east of the Mississippi River?

71. Of the nine handcart companies that journeyed to Utah, how many met with disaster?

72. How many congregations did Wilford Woodruff convert in the Fox Islands?

73. What specific kind of occupation shows up most often on nineteenth-century Mormon immigrant lists?

74. When new Governor Alfred Cumming entered Salt Lake City for the first time, in April 1858, what was unusual about it?

75. In what year did white men first enter Utah's Great Basin?

76. What was the Indian Relief Society?

77. Hiram Page, one of the Eight Witnesses, was rebuked for writing false revelations. By what means did he receive these "revelations"?

78. How long did the Mormon refugees from Jackson County stay in Clay County?

79. Lorenzo Snow spent five months surveying conditions of what groups of people?

80. Within one thousand, how many Saints emigrated from Great Britain to Nauvoo?

81. What were missionaries instructed to do (if prompted by the Holy Ghost) when people rejected them?

62. Section 2 (received on September 21, 1823, nearly five years before the next section)

63. Five thousand (*EN*, 12/83, p. 41)

64. John the Baptist (*HC*, 1:40)

65. Italy (*OHUM*, p. 64)

66. The Nauvoo Legion (*OHUM*, p. 38)

67. Joseph Smith (*OHUM*, p. 40)

68. Arizona (*ETN*, p. 407)

69. Wilford Woodruff (*ABM*, p. 399)

70. Two (sections 136 and 138—plus Official Declarations 1 and 2)

71. Only two (*OHUM*, pp. 108—9)

72. Two (*OHUM*, p. 95)

73. Miner (*OHUM*, p. 115)

74. The city was vacant, citizens having left because of Johnston's Army (*OHUM*, p. 91)

75. 1776 (*OHUM*, p. 2)

76. White sisters who met weekly to make clothes and bedding for the Indians (*ME*, p. 149)

77. A stone in his possession (D&C 28:11; *HC* 1:109—10)

78. Three years (*OHUM*, p. 31)

79. Various Indian tribes (*ETN*, p. 446)

80. Five thousand (*OHUM*, p. 35)

81. "Shake off the dust of your feet as a testimony against them" (D&C 24:15; 75:20)

82. Lorenzo Snow had the Book of Mormon translated into and published in what language?

83. Who was Zelph?

84. In which decade in the 1800s did the greatest number of emigrants travel from Great Britain to Utah?

85. What was the cost of printing the first five thousand copies of the Book of Mormon?

86. How many of the revelations in the Doctrine and Covenants were received in Salt Lake City?

87. Within five thousand, how many people were present when the Salt Lake Temple capstone was set in place?

88. The 1890 U.S. census showed that Mormons held a majority in what two western states?

89. How many pages of the Book of Mormon translation were lost?

90. Why did the Mormons withdraw their initial request for territorial government in Utah?

91. What happened to the population of Cedar City, Utah, after the nearby Mountain Meadows Massacre?

92. Who was Joseph Smith's scribe for most of the translation of the Book of Mormon?

93. Who was the first President of the Church born in Salt Lake City?

94. George Q. Cannon served as a counselor to how many Presidents of the Church?

95. According to the Prophet Joseph Smith, John the Beloved was then working among what people?

96. Where in each town did early pioneers gather to hear public announcements and see justice administered?

97. Where did Joseph Smith live when the work of translating the Book of Mormon began?

98. What U.S. president said, "Your cause is just, but I can do nothing for you"?

99. What section of the United States was reopened to missionary work in 1875, following the Civil War?

100. What did President John Taylor do about the $1.6 million owed to the Perpetual Emigration Fund in 1880?

101. Who showed the Book of Mormon plates to the Eight Witnesses?

102. Which President of the Church suffered from severe insomnia in his later years?

82. Italian (*ETN*, p. 443)

83. A "white Lamanite" whose bones were found in a mound during the Zion's Camp march (*HC*, 1:79−80)

84. The 1850s (*OHUM*, p. 106)

85. Three thousand dollars (*EN*, 12/83, p. 41)

86. Three (section 138 and Official Declarations 1 and 2)

87. Forty thousand (*ETN*, p. 432)

88. Utah and Idaho (*OHUM*, p. 114)

89. One hundred sixteen (D&C 3)

90. They learned that such an arrangement would mean government by outsiders (*OHUM*, pp. 82−83)

91. It dropped by more than half (*OHUM*, p. 67)

92. Oliver Cowdery

93. Heber J. Grant (*CA*, 1982, p. 95)

94. Four (*ES*, p. 33)

95. The Ten Tribes of Israel (*HC*, 1:176)

96. The "liberty pole," the pole that flew the national flag (*OHUM*, pp. 77−78)

97. Harmony, Pennsylvania

98. Martin Van Buren (*OHUM*, p. 38)

99. The South (*ETN*, p. 402)

100. He forgave half the indebtedness as part of the Church's Jubilee celebration (*OHUM*, p. 111)

101. Joseph Smith (*HC*, 1:57−58)

102. Wilford Woodruff (*ABM*, p. 401)

103. What unique thing do sections 15 and 16 of the Doctrine and Covenants have in common?

104. Who issued the infamous Extermination Order?

105. What woman served as Joseph Smith's scribe for a short time while he translated the Book of Mormon?

106. Who were in the Carthage Jail cell with Joseph Smith when he was murdered?

107. What unusual article of clothing was officially promoted in nineteenth-century Hebron, Utah?

108. In what year was the Relief Society first organized?

109. What name was the Church given when it was first organized?

110. Within twenty, how many people were in the initial pioneer group that journeyed to the Rocky Mountains?

111. What did Brigham Young plan to do if Johnston's Army entered Salt Lake City?

112. What Mormon militia hampered the movement of Johnston's Army as it approached Utah?

113. Who is the author of the statement, "As man now is, God once was: As God now is, man may become"?

114. In his presidential platform, Joseph Smith advocated abolition of slavery through what means?

115. The April 1980 general conference was unique in that part of it originated, not from Temple Square, but from what other site?

116. How long before his death did Joseph Smith prophesy that the Saints would be "driven to the Rocky Mountains"?

117. In November 1878, about two hundred non-Mormon women of Salt Lake held a mass meeting for what purpose?

118. What new feature of the 1876 edition of the Doctrine and Covenants made it similar in format to the Bible?

119. Where was the Mormon Battalion located when its members helped to build Fort Moore?

120. How many nations were represented at Utah's twenty-fourth of July celebration in 1880?

121. What river were Joseph Smith and Oliver Cowdery baptized in?

122. In which city were more of the sections in the Doctrine and Covenants received than in any other city?

123. What group provided the initial police system in Utah?

103. Their wording is almost identical

104. Governor Lilburn Boggs of Missouri (*OHUM*, p. 31)

105. His wife Emma (*JSR*, p. 88)

106. Hyrum Smith, John Taylor, and Willard Richards

107. Wooden shoes (*MGI*, p. 42)

108. 1842 (*HC*, 4:552–53)

109. The Church of Christ (D&C 20:1)

110. 148 (*OHUM*, p. 52)

111. Burn the city to the ground (*OHUM*, p. 91)

112. The Nauvoo Legion (*OHUM*, p. 90)

113. Lorenzo Snow

114. By purchasing the slaves from their owners, then setting them free (*OHUM*, p. 43)

115. The Peter Whitmer farm in Fayette, New York (where the Church was organized 150 years earlier)

116. Two years (*OHUM*, pp. 41–42)

117. To request that statehood for Utah be delayed until polygamy was abolished (*ETN*, p. 402)

118. The sections were divided into verses

119. Los Angeles, California (*OHUM*, p. 51)

120. Twenty-three (*ETN*, p. 410)

121. The Susquehanna River, near Harmony, Pennsylvania (D&C 13)

122. Kirtland, Ohio (forty-six revelations)

123. The Nauvoo Legion (*OHUM*, p. 79)

124. Which Apostle was appointed to preside over England in 1848?

125. Who was the next person to be baptized after Oliver Cowdery and Joseph Smith?

126. Within five years, when did the transcontinental railroad come to Utah?

127. Who served as a member of the First Council of the Seventy for the longest time?

128. What was the family relationship between Joseph Fielding Smith and Apostle Hyrum Mack Smith?

129. Within fifty, how many Mormon settlements did the Saints establish by 1890?

130. What British port city was the main point of debarkation for Mormon emigrants?

131. How large were the home lots in Joseph Smith's plan for the City of Zion?

132. Why was the area of Palmyra, New York, called the "Burned Over District" when the Smiths moved there in 1816?

133. In which state were more of the sections in the Doctrine and Covenants received than in any other state?

134. Why were colonists sent to the Virgin River Valley in 1857?

135. Within $1 million, what were the property losses of the Mormons who were driven from Missouri?

136. Next to Smith, which family name has had the most General Authorities?

137. Besides the plates of the Book of Mormon, what four items were the Three Witnesses promised they would be privileged to see?

138. When Moroni appeared to Joseph Smith on September 21–22, 1823, which three Old Testament prophets did he quote?

139. John Taylor arranged to have the Book of Mormon published in two different languages. Name one.

140. President Brigham Young proclaimed that there should be no private ownership of what three natural resources?

141. When Mormon emigrants arrived in America, who usually met them to help them continue their journey to Salt Lake City?

142. How long before his death did Joseph Smith organize an exploration company to seek a refuge for the Saints in the West?

143. How long were the Saints in Utah before they organized the Perpetual Emigration Fund to help other emigrants?

124. Orson Pratt (*OHUM*, p. 96)

125. Samuel H. Smith, Joseph's brother (*HC*, 1:44)

126. 1869 (*OHUM*, p. 73)

127. Levi Edgar Young — fifty-four years (*MMZ*, p. 439)

128. Brothers (*ABM*, p. 304)

129. Over six hundred — in nine western states and two foreign countries (*OHUM*, pp. 73–74)

130. Liverpool, England (*OHUM*, p. 113)

131. A half-acre each (*OHUM*, p. 30)

132. Because of the intensity of religious revivalism sweeping the area (*OHUM*, p. 21)

133. Ohio (sixty-four revelations)

134. To establish a "cotton mission" (*OHUM*, p. 69)

135. $2 million (*OHUM*, p. 31)

136. Young (*MMZ*, p. 528)

137. The Urim and Thummim, the accompanying breastplate, the sword of Laban, and the Liahona (D&C 17:1)

138. Malachi, Isaiah, and Joel (JS-H 1:36–41)

139. French and German (*ETN*, p. 414)

140. Water, timber, and land (*CHC*, 3:269)

141. Perpetual Emigration Fund agents (*OHUM*, p. 105)

142. Four months (*OHUM*, p. 42)

143. Two years (*OHUM*, p. 63)

144. Besides Church President, which General Authority office was the first to be filled in the 1830s?

145. During the Church's Jubilee Conference, what did the Relief Society loan to the brethren of the Church?

146. Where was Joseph Smith living when he introduced ordinance work for the dead?

147. Within five, in what year did the Church publicly announce the doctrine of plural marriage?

148. Where was Joseph Smith when the Saints were driven from Missouri?

149. Who was chosen as the presiding quorum of the Church at the general conference in 1877?

150. What was the title of the first published collection of revelations that later became the Doctrine and Covenants?

151. What was Joseph Smith's military rank in the Nauvoo Legion?

152. Within fifty, how many Mormon colonies had been established in the West by the time Brigham Young died?

153. After the death of Joseph Smith, what eastern city did the Twelve gather at prior to returning to Nauvoo?

154. Who dedicated the Salt Lake Valley for settlement by the Saints?

155. Of all those in the initial pioneer group that journeyed to the Rocky Mountains, how many were women?

156. Who was commander of the Nauvoo Legion when Johnston's Army marched on Utah?

157. Who was the first governor of the Utah Territory?

158. In which section of the Doctrine and Covenants are the sacramental prayers found?

159. What were the "twin relics of barbarism" the Republican Party vowed in 1856 to destroy?

160. How many General Authorities lived to be one hundred years old?

161. According to the Prophet Joseph Smith, an evangelist is a what?

162. When Moroni appeared to Joseph Smith on September 21 – 22, 1823, which book of the New Testament did he quote from?

163. In what decade in the 1800s did the Church undergo a broad reform movement?

164. What served as a schoolhouse in Salt Lake City in October 1847?

165. A priest may ordain others to what priesthood offices?

144. Presiding Bishop (*OHUM*, p. 25)

145. Seed wheat (34,761 bushels) (*CHC*, 5:593)

146. Nauvoo, Illinois (*OHUM*, p. 35)

147. 1852 (*OHUM*, p. 85)

148. Imprisoned in Liberty Jail (*OHUM*, p. 32)

149. The Quorum of the Twelve (*ETN*, p. 394)

150. The Book of Commandments

151. Lieutenant General (*OHUM*, p. 38)

152. Over 360 (*OHUM*, p. 73)

153. Boston (*ETN*, p. 425)

154. Orson Pratt (*OHUM*, p. 56)

155. Five (*OHUM*, p. 52)

156. Daniel H. Wells (*OHUM*, p. 90)

157. Brigham Young (*OHUM*, p. 72)

158. Section 20 (Verses 75−79)

159. Slavery and polygamy (*OHUM*, p. 89)

160. None

161. A patriarch (*HC*, 3:381)

162. Acts (JS-H 1:40)

163. 1850s (*OHUM*, p. 86)

164. A tent (*OHUM*, p. 125)

165. He may ordain other priests, teachers, and deacons (D&C 20:54)

166. What group of people was Stephen A. Douglas referring to when he said they were "an ulcer on the body politic" that should be cut out?

167. What day of the week was fast day through most of the nineteenth century?

168. Who was the first President of the Quorum of the Twelve?

169. What is the difference between the sacramental prayers given in 1830 and the prayers we use today?

170. What was "the year without a summer"?

171. Who contracted to print the first edition of the Book of Mormon?

172. What important event occurred on May 15, 1829?

173. In which section of the Doctrine and Covenants is the baptismal prayer found?

174. What Church body sponsored Joseph Smith for the presidency of the United States and later supervised the exodus to Utah?

175. What was the symbol of the Mormon state of Deseret?

176. When the Mormons settled in Utah, what did they call the overall geographic area?

177. The failure of what banking organization led to widespread apostasy in 1837 in Kirtland, Ohio?

178. In what year did Joseph Smith run for the U.S. presidency?

179. Why did Brigham Young send Saints to establish a settlement in Cedar City, Utah?

180. Evidence from section 20 of the Doctrine and Covenants suggests that the Lord was born on what day of the year?

181. Why were Church members reluctant to pay their tithing by 1890?

182. When the Church was organized in 1830 it included only four priesthood offices. What were they?

183. What happened to the men who shot and killed missionary Joseph Standing?

184. Why were special missionaries sent out in April 1844?

185. What U.S. president did Joseph Smith visit in seeking reparation for the Saints' Missouri losses?

186. On what date was the Church formally organized?

187. Why was fast day changed from Thursday to Sunday in 1896?

166. The Mormons (*OHUM*, p. 89)

167. Thursdays—the first Thursday of the month (*OHUM*, p. 125)

168. Thomas B. Marsh (*ABM*, p. 182)

169. The word *water* is substituted for *wine* (see D&C 27:2)

170. 1816, a year of severe frosts and crop failures that forced the Smith family to move from Vermont to Palmyra, New York (*EN*, 1/83, p. 65)

171. Egbert B. Grandin (*EN*, 12/83, p. 41)

172. The Aaronic Priesthood was restored (D&C 13)

173. Section 20 (verses 72–74)

174. The Council of Fifty (*OHUM*, p. 40)

175. The beehive (*OHUM*, p. 137)

176. Upper California (*OHUM*, p. 62)

177. The Kirtland Safety Society, which was owned by the Church (*OHUM*, p. 28)

178. 1844 (*OHUM*, p. 43)

179. To establish an "iron mission" (*OHUM*, p. 66)

180. April 6 (D&C 20:1; section heading)

181. Church monies were being confiscated by the U.S. Government (*ETN*, p. 454)

182. Deacon, teacher, priest, and elder (D&C 20:48)

183. They were tried and found not guilty (*ETN*, p. 405)

184. To promote Joseph Smith as president of the United States (*OHUM*, p. 43)

185. Martin Van Buren (*OHUM*, p. 38)

186. April 6, 1830 (D&C 20:1)

187. Many Saints were employed by gentile merchants and were unable to attend fast meeting (*ETN*, p. 435)

188. Who did the Lord designate as the "first preacher of the Church"?

189. What group of Mormons participated in the discovery of gold at Sutter's Fort, California?

190. When the Saints were driven out of Missouri, where did they go?

191. At the first conference of the Church, which two sections of the D&C became the first modern revelations to be "canonized"?

192. Within ten thousand, how many adult Saints immigrated to Utah from 1847 to 1887?

193. Who wrote revolutionary books on dry farming and irrigation before becoming an Apostle?

194. How many Presidents of the Church have had a son serve as President of the Quorum of the Twelve?

195. Why wasn't Joseph Smith permitted to retranslate the material in the lost 116 pages of the Book of Mormon manuscript?

196. How many sections of the Doctrine and Covenants were received before the Church was organized?

197. Who invited the Mormons to establish a settlement in the area of Manti, Utah?

198. What was the Mormon name for Commerce, Illinois?

199. What happened to all Church real estate holdings over $50,000 with the Anti-Bigamy Law of 1862?

200. When John the Baptist conferred the Aaronic Priesthood on Joseph Smith and Oliver Cowdery, whose direction was he acting under?

201. Section 25 is the only section of the Doctrine and Covenants directed specifically to a woman. What was her name?

202. What Apostle translated the Book of Mormon into the Deseret Alphabet?

203. What town, named after a U.S. president, was the initial territorial capital of Utah?

204. On what date was the Aaronic Priesthood restored?

205. Where was Joseph Smith living when he wrote the Articles of Faith?

206. Within one hundred, how many people did Heber C. Kimball and his associates baptize in their first eight months in England in 1837?

207. How many of the hosts of heaven joined Satan in his rebellion against God?

188. Oliver Cowdery (D&C 21:12)

189. The Mormon Battalion (*OHUM*, p. 51)

190. Illinois (*OHUM*, p. 33)

191. Sections 20 and 22

192. Eighty-five thousand (not counting thousands of children not included on the passenger lists) (*OHUM*, p. 111)

193. John A Widtsoe (*MMZ*, p. 258)

194. Two—Brigham Young and Joseph F. Smith

195. Because the Prophet's enemies could have altered the wording in the missing original in order to discredit him (D&C 10:10—19, 31—32)

196. Eighteen

197. Chief Joseph Walker (*OHUM*, p. 63)

198. Nauvoo (*OHUM*, p. 33)

199. They were forfeited to the U.S. government (*ETN*, p. 395)

200. Peter, James, and John (D&C 13)

201. Emma Smith

202. Orson Pratt (*MMZ*, p. 207)

203. Fillmore, in Millard County (*OHUM*, p. 67)

204. May 15, 1829

205. Nauvoo, Illinois (*OHUM*, p. 36)

206. Two thousand (*OHUM*, p. 95)

207. One-third (D&C 29:36)

208. How old was the Prophet Joseph Smith when he was murdered?

209. Who was the first bishop in the Church?

210. Where did this familiar statement originate: "A religion that does not require the sacrifice of all things never has power sufficient to produce the faith necessary unto life and salvation"?

211. During the Church's Jubilee Conference, what did President Taylor urge the Church and individuals to free worthy people of?

212. Which U.S. president did Brigham Young appeal to in seeking an official western refuge for the Saints?

213. Was Joseph Smith older or younger than his brother Hyrum?

214. On what day of the week was the Church formally organized?

215. Satan is not given power to tempt whom?

216. How did the Church membership in England compare to that in Utah in 1850?

217. How long did the Quorum of the Twelve preside over the Church after Brigham Young died?

218. The earliest fragment known to exist from the original dictated manuscript of the Book of Mormon contains ten words from which book?

219. Within two, how many settlements did the Mormons establish in northern Mexico?

220. What area, originally dedicated by Orson Hyde was rededicated by George A. Smith in 1873?

221. What was Oliver Cowdery's profession when he first met Joseph Smith?

222. Who was the first secretary of the state of Deseret?

223. What city scrved as a seaport for the provisional state of Deseret?

224. In the October 1901 general conference, President Snow spoke at length on the jurisdiction and responsibility of what group of priesthood brethren?

225. Which one of the Three Witnesses died in Utah?

226. Utah's original seed crop of sugar beets came from what European country?

227. Who served the longest in the First Presidency?

228. Next to Brigham Young, who served the longest as President of the Church?

229. Which edition of the *Doctrine and Covenants* first bore that title?

208. Thirty-eight and a half years old

209. Edward Partridge (D&C 41:9)

210. In the *Lectures on Faith* (*LF*, p. 58)

211. Debts (*CHC*, 5:593)

212. James K. Polk (*OHUM*, p. 45)

213. Younger, by almost six years

214. Tuesday

215. "Little children, until they begin to become accountable" (D&C 29:47)

216. England had more than twice as many members as Utah (*OHUM*, p. 98)

217. Three years (*ETN*, p. 394)

218. Mosiah (Chapter 2, verses 6 – 7 and 17 – 18) (*EN*, 12/83, p. 38)

219. Eight (*OHUM*, p. 73)

220. The Holy Land (*ETN*, p. 445)

221. He was a school teacher (*HC*, 1:32)

222. Willard Richards (*OHUM*, p. 81)

223. San Diego (*OHUM*, p. 80)

224. Bishops and stake presidents (*TN*, p. 459)

225. Martin Harris

226. France (*OHUM*, p. 64)

227. Joseph F. Smith (*ABM*, p. 189)

228. Heber J. Grant (*MMZ*, p. 6)

229. The 1835 edition

230. Which two sections of the Doctrine and Covenants were called the "Articles and Covenants" and were often reviewed at early conferences?

231. What is astronomically significant about the days on which the angel Moroni appeared to Joseph Smith in the years from 1823 to 1827?

232. Within five, how many members of the Church attended the first conference on June 9, 1830?

233. The practice of voting to accept or reject the decisions of Church leaders is called "government by _____ _____."

234. What is the most famous Nevada community established by the early Mormons?

235. How many days did the first Pioneer Day celebration last?

236. Who wrote the *Comprehensive History of the Church?*

237. When the Church reinstituted the law of consecration in the 1850s, what portion of the members deeded their property to the Church?

238. A marble monument in Windsor County, Vermont, marks the birthplace of Joseph Smith. Why is it 38½ feet high?

239. Four of the Eight Witnesses to the Book of Mormon were from what family?

240. What did the Prophet Joseph Smith say was the "keystone of our religion"?

241. The early Utah Church meetinghouse usually doubled as what?

242. Who said to Joseph Smith, "It mattereth not what ye shall eat or what ye shall drink when ye partake of the sacrament"?

243. What was the scientific explanation given in 1882 by *Physiognomy Illustrated* for the Mormon penchant for polygamy?

244. Who issued the extermination order against the Saints in Missouri in October 1838?

245. Within five, how many yards of cotton did the initial quart of seed planted in Utah yield?

246. What learning institution was established in Salt Lake City in 1850?

247. Section 7 of the Doctrine and Covenants is a translation of a record written on parchment by whom?

248. Within twenty, how many Mormon settlements had been established in the Great Basin area by 1858?

249. Within $50,000, how much tithing was the Church collecting each year during the 1880s?

230. Sections 20 and 22 (*DCOMS* p. 3)

231. Each one was the day of the autumn equinox (Sept. 21 or 22)

232. Twenty-seven (*OHUM*, p. 22)

233. "Common consent" (D&C 26:2)

234. Las Vegas (*OHUM*, p. 71)

235. Five days (July 20 through July 24, 1897) (*ETN*, p. 436)

236. B.H. Roberts (*MMZ*, p. 425)

237. One-third (*OHUM*, p. 86)

238. One foot for each year of the prophet's life (*OHUM*, p. 18)

239. The Whitmer family

240. The Book of Mormon (*HC*, 4:461)

241. A schoolhouse (*OHUM*, p. 61)

242. A "heavenly messenger" (*HC*, 1:106; D&C 27, section head)

243. The narrow aperture of the Mormon eye (*MGI*, p. 53)

244. Governor Lilburn W. Boggs (*HC*, 3:175)

245. Thirty (*OHUM*, p. 69)

246. The University of Deseret (*OHUM*, p. 126)

247. John the Beloved

248. Nearly 150 (*OHUM*, p. 61)

249. $500,000 (*ETN*, p. 452)

250. Who did Charles Dickens describe as "the pick and flower of England"?

251. Before rail transportation went to the West, what American port city did Mormon emigrants usually sail to?

252. Since Brigham Young was sick, who led the first group of Saints on the last leg of their trip to the Salt Lake Valley?

253. How was land generally divided among the early pioneer settlers in Utah?

254. How was the Salt Lake Temple capstone dropped into place?

255. Who did the English Saints ask to help them in emigrating to America in 1847?

256. What country owned the Salt Lake Valley when the Mormons settled there?

257. Which section of the Doctrine and Covenants is known as "the Law of the Church"?

258. In editions of the Doctrine and Covenants prior to 1981, the word "Cainhannoch" referred to what?

259. How many times did Joseph Smith ask the Lord to let Martin Harris take the first 116 pages of the Book of Mormon translation?

260. What was the name of the anti-Mormon political organization which existed in Utah from 1904 to 1911?

261. How many people named *Joseph Smith* have been General Authorities?

262. How many of Hyrum Smith's descendants have been Presidents of the Church?

263. Which priesthood holds the "keys of the ministering of angels"?

264. Which two Presidents of the Church were born in Vermont?

265. What was another name for the Council of the Kingdom?

266. According to some anti-Mormons, what Solomon Spaulding manuscript did Joseph Smith plagiarize in writing the Book of Mormon?

267. In 1830, who was Parley P. Pratt sent on a mission to when he helped convert Sidney Rigdon and hundreds of Campbellites?

268. What did the Mormons call present-day Council Bluffs, Iowa, when they temporarily halted there in their 1846 westward trek?

269. What two Mormon sciensists served as president of the University of Utah and later became Apostles?

250. Mormon emigrants (*OHUM*, p. 112)

251. New Orleans (*OHUM*, pp. 104–5)

252. Orson Pratt (*OHUM*, p. 55)

253. By drawing lots (*OHUM*, p. 59)

254. Wilford Woodruff pressed an electric button, which caused it to drop (*ETN*, p. 432)

255. Queen Victoria (*OHUM*, p. 100)

256. Mexico (*OHUM*, p. 58)

257. Section 42

258. New York (D&C 104:81)

259. Three (*HC*, 1:21)

260. American Party (*ECH*, p. 512)

261. Five (*MMZ*, p. 528)

262. Two (his son and grandson, Joseph F. Smith and Joseph Fielding Smith)

263. The Aaronic Priesthood (D&C 13)

264. Joseph Smith and Brigham Young

265. The Council of Fifty (*OHUM*, p. 40)

266. "The Manuscript Found" (*MD*, p. 749)

267. The Lamanites (*OHUM*, pp. 22–23)

268. Kanesville, after non-Mormon friend Col. Thomas Kane (*OHUM*, p. 18)

269. James E. Talmage, John A. Widtsoe

270. What was the physical relationship of Kanesville and Winter Quarters, the two settlements where the Mormons stopped on their way west?

271. To whom was the Prophet Joseph Smith's last recorded prophecy directed?

272. What was Brigham Young sick with when he first sighted the Salt Lake Valley?

273. Half of the revelations given through Joseph Smith before he received the Melchizedek Priesthood came by what means?

274. On July 2, 1899, a solemn assembly was held in the Salt Lake Temple with all the General Authorities present. Within five, how many were there?

275. What verse of scripture from the New Testament led young Joseph Smith to go to the woods to pray for wisdom?

276. Who served the longest as a General Authority?

277. Who was the "first elder of the Church"?

278. The Lord said, "In the mouth of____witnesses shall every word be established." How many witnesses did he specify?

279. Where did Relief Societies often meet until 1921?

280. How many sections of the Doctrine and Covenants did Joseph Smith receive through the angel Moroni?

281. What hymn did John Taylor sing for the Prophet Joseph Smith in the Carthage Jail less than two hours before the martyrdom?

282. Who assisted Joseph Smith when, in 1830, he began the work of collecting, copying, and arranging the revelations for publication?

283. Which President of the Church was not born in the United States?

284. What Israelite celebration did the Church emulate in its fiftieth year?

285. Section 1 of the Doctrine and Covenants is known as what?

286. Why did the Mormons travel on the north side of the Platte River rather than the south side, as most pioneer companies did?

287. During the first Pioneer Day celebration in 1897, what were the remaining 650 pioneers of 1847 given?

288. Which General Authority took charge of the forced exodus of the Saints from Missouri?

270. They were located on opposite sides of the Missouri River (*OHUM*, p. 49)

271. Dan Jones (*HC*, 6:601)

272. "Mountain fever" (*OHUM*, p. 55)

273. The Urim and Thummim (*DCOMS*, p. 3)

274. Twenty-six (*ETN*, p. 455)

275. James 1:5 (JS-H 1:11)

276. David O. McKay (*ABM*, p. 189)

277. Joseph Smith (D&C 20:1; JS-H 1:72)

278. Two or three (D&C 6:28)

279. In Relief Society halls, separate buildings usually located near the ward chapel (*ME*, p. 215)

280. One (Section 2)

281. "A Poor Wayfaring Man of Grief" (*HC*, 6:614−15)

282. John Whitmer (*HC*, 1:104)

283. President John Taylor (born in England)

284. The Jubilee Year (*ETN*, p. 409)

285. The Lord's Preface

286. They wanted to be safely separated from other travelers (*OHUM*, pp. 52−53)

287. Solid gold medals (*ETN*, p. 436)

288. Brigham Young (*OHUM*, p. 32)

289. In what town was the first edition of the Book of Mormon printed?

290. Within two, how many times did Utah petition Congress for statehood between 1851 and 1890?

291. Some of the brethren of Zion's Camp were about to kill what until Joseph Smith intervened?

292. Section 111 is the only revelation in the Doctrine and Covenants that was received in a city by an ocean. What was that city?

293. What two men served as Assistant President of the Church?

294. Where was water business commonly conducted in pioneer Utah?

295. When did Martin Harris exclaim, " 'Tis enough; 'tis enough; mine eyes have beheld; mine eyes have beheld"?

296. Who were the first two Apostles in the Church?

297. What non-Mormon friend of Brigham Young visited Utah to help negotiate during the Utah War?

298. What famous explorer named Utah's Great Basin?

299. What was the likely cause of the unusually cold weather in 1816 that forced the Smith family to move from Vermont to New York?

300. Who chose the first Quorum of the Twelve Apostles in 1835?

Simpler Questions for Use as Needed

301. What is the place called where Joseph Smith first went to pray about which church to join?

302. What saved John Taylor's life when a bullet fired by the mob at the Carthage Jail struck him in the chest?

303. What is the revelation called that teaches us not to smoke or drink liquor?

304. Which General Authority took charge of the Saints when they moved to the West—Brigham Young, Joseph Smith, or John Taylor?

305. Was the first temple built in New York, Kirtland, or Nauvoo?

306. The Lord had an angel show the golden plates to three witnesses. Name one of them.

307. When Joseph Smith and Oliver Cowdery prayed about baptism, a messenger came to them. Who was it?

289. Palmyra, New York

290. Nine (*OHUM*, p. 84)

291. "Three massasaugas or prarie rattlesnakes (*HC*, 2:71)

292. Salem, Massachusetts

293. Oliver Cowdery and Hyrum Smith (*MMZ*, p. 71)

294. In priesthood meeting (*ME*, p. 211)

295. When the angel showed him the plates of the Book of Mormon (*HC*, 1:55)

296. Joseph Smith and Oliver Cowdery (D&C 20:2−3)

297. Col. Thomas Kane (*OHUM*, p. 91)

298. John C. Fremont (*OHUM*, p. 2)

299. Shading of the sun's rays caused by volcanic ash from the eruption of Mount Tambora, east of Java, in April 1815 (*EN*, 1/83, p. 65)

300. The Three Witnesses: David Whitmer, Oliver Cowdery, and Martin Harris (*HC*, 2:186−87)

301. The Sacred Grove

302. The bullet hit his watch (*HC*, 6:618, 620)

303. The Word of Wisdom (*SOOC*, p. 67)

304. Brigham Young (*OHUM*, p. 32)

305. Kirtland

306. Martin Harris, Oliver Cowdery, and David Whitmer (*SOOC*, p. 33)

307. John the Baptist (*SOOC*, p. 29)

308. How many times did the angel Moroni visit Joseph Smith the first night?

309. How old was Joseph Smith when the angel Moroni first visited him — fifteen, sixteen or seventeen?

310. How many General Authorities have lived to be one hundred years old?

311. Joseph received the records of Abraham from a strange place. Were they found in a hollow tree, some mummy coffins, a bottle, or a cave?

312. Who was the first President of the Church?

313. Who baptized Joseph Smith?

314. Martin Harris took 116 pages of the Book of Mormon to show to his family. What happened to them?

315. What did Moroni come to tell Joseph Smith about?

316. Name the President of the Church who ran for President of the United States.

317. How old was Joseph Smith when he became President of the Church — twenty-one, twenty-six, or thirty-two?

318. In which month was The Church of Jesus Christ of Latter-day Saints organized?

319. Where did the children meet for school in Salt Lake City in October 1847 — a house, a tent, a fort, or a store?

320. How many years did it take to build the Kirtland temple — three, five, or ten?

321. About how old was Joseph Smith when he had the vision in the Sacred Grove?

322. True or false: President David O. McKay was once an English teacher.

323. Who served the longest as President of the Church — Brigham Young, Heber J. Grant, David O. McKay, or Harold B. Lee?

324. What was Brigham Young sick with when he first sighted the Salt Lake Valley — mountain fever, malaria, or snake bite poison?

325. Was the city of Nauvoo built in a forest, on a swamp, or in the mountains?

326. Name the three degrees of glory that Joseph Smith and Sidney Rigdon saw in a vision.

327. What was the first name of Joseph Smith's wife?

328. Which of Joseph Smith's brothers was killed with him at Carthage Jail?

329. Joseph Smith translated the record of Abraham. What book of scripture is that record found in today?

330. Before Sidney Rigdon joined the Church, was he a farmer, a pastor, or a blacksmith?

308. Three times (plus once more in the morning) (*SOOC*, p. 13)

309. Seventeen years old (*SOOC*, p. 13)

310. None

311. Some mummy coffins from Egypt (*SOOC*, p. 95)

312. Joseph Smith

313. Oliver Cowdery (*SOOC*, p. 30)

314. They were lost (*SOOC*, p. 21)

315. The Golden Plates (*SOOC*, p. 11)

316. Joseph Smith

317. Twenty-six

318. April (April 6, 1830)

319. A tent (*OHUM*, p. 125)

320. Three years (*SOOC*, p. 70)

321. About fourteen years old (*SOOC*, p. 4)

322. True

323. Brigham Young

324. Mountain fever (*OHUM*, p. 55)

325. On a swamp (*SOOC*, p. 148)

326. Celestial, terrestrial, and telestial (*SOOC*, p. 64)

327. Emma

328. Hyrum Smith

329. The Pearl of Great Price (*SOOC*, p. 95)

330. A pastor (*SOOC*, p. 55)

331. Joseph Smith sent missionaries westward to preach the gospel to what group of people?

332. When Joseph Smith was a boy, he had to have an operation on what part of his body?

333. Who were the two personages Joseph Smith saw when he prayed in the Sacred Grove?

334. Was Brigham Young a carpenter, a teacher, or a printer before he became Church President?

335. True or false: Brigham Young was the father of over fifty children.

336. How much did it cost to publish the first five thousand copies of the Book of Mormon — $500, $1,000, or $3,000?

337. A mob stripped Joseph Smith and stuck hot tar on his body. What did they put over the tar?

338. What day of the week was fast day in the early days of the Church — Sunday, Thursday, Friday, or Saturday?

339. True or false: The Kirtland temple was also used as a meetinghouse and even children could enter it.

340. Who was the first angel who appeared to Joseph Smith?

341. Were Joseph Smith's eyes blue or brown?

342. True or false: Apostles Orson Pratt and Parley P. Pratt were brothers.

343. Who arranged the first hymn book for the Church?

344. Three ancient Apostles came to Joseph Smith and Oliver Cowdery to give them the Melchizedek Priesthood. Who were they?

345. Joseph had many revelations from the Lord. Which book of scripture are they recorded in?

346. Where were the golden plates hidden?

347. Joseph F. Smith became the sixth President of the Church. Who was his famous uncle?

348. Who was President of the Church when Abraham Lincoln was president of the United States — Brigham Young, John Taylor, or Wilford Woodruff?

349. When Mormons sailing from Europe to America prayed for a violent storm to end, what happened?

350. As the city of Nauvoo grew and prospered, was it bigger or smaller than Chicago?

331. The Lamanites (Indians)
(*SOOC*, p. 55)

332. His leg (*SOOC*, p. 2)

333. Heavenly Father and Jesus
Christ (*SOOC*, p. 7)

334. Carpenter

335. True

336. $3,000 (*SOOC*, p. 39)

337. Feathers

338. Thursdays—the first Thursday of the month (*OHUM*,
p. 125)

339. True (*SOOC*, p. 70)

340. Moroni (*SOOC*, p. 10)

341. Blue

342. True

343. Emma Smith, Joseph's wife
(*SOOC*, p. 51)

344. Peter, James and John
(*SOOC*, p. 31)

345. Doctrine and Covenants

346. In the Hill Cumorah (*SOOC*,
p. 11)

347. Joseph Smith

348. Brigham Young

349. The storm stopped (*OHUM*,
p. 103)

350. Bigger—it was the largest
city in Illinois. Chicago was
a small trading post.
(*SOOC*, p. 149)

PART 5 People

1. Within ten years, how old was Maria Martinez, a Zuni Indian, when she went through the Mesa Arizona Temple?

2. Who discovered the world's oldest bird, as well as the first dinosaur eggs?

3. Did Jean Saubert win a gold, silver, or bronze medal, or no medal at all, in the 1964 Winter Olympics?

4. Dolores Lier was national skating champion in what country?

5. Which President of the Church was the oldest when he was ordained an Apostle?

6. True or false: President Kimball started the Family Home Evening program.

7. How did Carl "Star" Nelson profoundly help the Church genealogical effort?

8. What world-class runner worked for U.S. Steel Geneva Works in Orem, Utah?

9. What boxer was Gene Fullmer named after?

10. Who was a member of the Los Angeles Rams's "Fearsome Foursome"?

11. Who won several *Deseret News* Marathons in a row?

12. Former BYU assistant football coach Ted Tollner is now head coach at what major west-coast university?

13. Who was sustained as an Apostle the same day as Spencer W. Kimball?

14. Who did Bruce Hafen replace as president of Ricks College?

15. Who wrote *High Finance on a Low Budget?*

16. Who is the senior Apostle among Boyd K. Packer, Thomas S. Monson, and Marvin J. Ashton?

17. What did scientist Don Lind become in 1966?

18. Bertha S. Reeder was the president of what Church auxiliary from 1948 to 1961?

19. Who wrote *The Art of Homemaking?*

20. Sisters Connie Gerrard and Judy Gerrard Haeder were secretaries to what two top government men in 1967?

21. What was Karl Tucker's occupation when BYU hired him as their golf coach in the early 1960s?

22. What was unique about the temple presidencies of Selvoy Boyer, George England, and LeRoy Buckmiller, presidents of the London Temple from 1958 to 1968?

1. One hundred and fourteen years old (*CN*, 12/13/69, p. 4)

2. "Dinosaur Jim" Jenson (*BYU*, 12/83, p. 15)

3. Silver (*MA II*, p. 64)

4. Switzerland (*MA II*, p. 162)

5. President Kimball—age forty-eight (*CA*, 1980, p. 70)

6. False (It was started by President Joseph F. Smith.)

7. He helped provide the technical know-how for establishing the genealogical microfilm system (*BYU*, 12/83, p. 47)

8. Paul Cummings (*MA*, p. 113)

9. Gene Tunney (*WW*, p. 1)

10. Merlin Olsen (*MA II*, p. 45)

11. Demetrio Cabanillas (*CA*, 1982, p. 253)

12. University of Southern California (*BYU*, 4/83, p. 19)

13. Ezra Taft Benson

14. Henry B. Eyring (*EN*, 1/78, p. 78)

15. Mark Skousen (*BYU*, 3/82, p. 25)

16. Thomas S. Monson

17. An astronaut (*WW*, p. 36)

18. YWMIA (*CA*, 1980, p. 268)

19. Daryl V. Hoole

20. Lyndon B. Johnson and Hubert Humphrey (*CN*, 8/5/67, p. 6)

21. He was a junior high school teacher and coach (*GMBYUS*, p. 43)

22. None of those presidents had second counselors (*CA*, 1975, p. F8)

23. What future General Authority played on the 1951 NIT Tournament-winning BYU basketball team?

24. Who wrote a book called *Pure Golf?*

25. What professional position did Dr. James Mason hold as of 1984?

26. Suresh Chander Verma is believed to be the first LDS missionary from what country?

27. What General Authority served as managing director of Mormon pavilions at four different world fairs?

28. What publication was founded by Frances Lee Menlove?

29. What well-known LDS scientist received the National Medal of Science from President Lyndon B. Johnson in 1967?

30. What General Authority wrote *The Gift of Self?*

31. How old was Elder Russell Nelson when he became a medical doctor?

32. Who was the first Mormon to start as a National Football League quarterback?

33. Who was serving as president of the Boston Stake when he was called to be a General Authority in 1969?

34. What professional baseball player was nicknamed "the Deacon"?

35. Within five, how many years did Larry Lee work for Western Airlines before he became its president?

36. Who served as national commissioner of the Federal Housing Administration before his call as an Assistant to the Twelve?

37. Whose talks were collected in *Conference Classics?*

38. What BYU basketball player was known as "the Doctor" by his teammates?

39. By what name is Robert Parker more commonly known?

40. How many times was Henry Marsh an All-American in the steeplechase and cross-country runs?

41. Name the last U.S. president to be a distant cousin to President Kimball.

42. Who was the first native Utahn named first-team All-American quarterback?

43. Most of the Presidents of the Church were in what decade of their lives when they became President?

44. Who was Gene Fullmer's last fight against?

45. Kim Taylor is a star athlete in what sport?

46. Pedro Casares represented what country in the 1984 Olympics?

23. Loren C. Dunn (*MMZ*, p. 264)

24. Johnny Miller (*CA*, 1978, p. 18)

25. Director of National Center for Disease Control (*DN*, 3/29/85, p. 18B)

26. India (*CN*, 8/6/77, p. 5)

27. Bernard P. Brockbank (*CA*, 1982, p. 93)

28. *Dialogue* (*CA*, 1974, p. 48)

29. Dr. Henry Eyring (*CN*, 2/11/67, p. 6)

30. Marion D. Hanks

31. Twenty-two (*EN*, 6/84, p. 10)

32. Danny White (Dallas Cowboys) (*CN*, 12/27/80, p. 5)

33. L. Tom Perry (*MMZ*, p. 300)

34. Vernon Law (*MA* II, p. 96)

35. Forty (*TP*, 2/84, p. 16)

36. Franklin D. Richards (*MMZ*, p. 344)

37. Elder Thomas S. Monson's

38. Devin Durrant (*MA II*, p. 29)

39. Butch Cassidy (*ABM*, p. 62)

40. Five (*MA*, p. 59)

41. Gerald Ford (*NS*, p. 60)

42. Gifford Nielsen (*MA*, p. 33)

43. Their seventies

44. Dick Tiger

45. Gymnastics (*MA II*, p. 14)

46. Argentina (*EN*, 10/84, p. 78)

47. In 1984, Paula Meyers Pope won Olympic medals in what sport?

48. How long did Homer Harvey Holcomb reign as the undefeated World Champion Cowboy?

49. Dean Jessee compiled what important book concerning Joseph Smith?

50. How did Elder F. Burton Howard's children learn of their father's call to the First Quorum of the Seventy?

51. Forty-eight hours after returning home from presiding over the Northern England Mission, what calling did Royden Derrick receive?

52. What position did David M. Kennedy hold in President Richard Nixon's cabinet?

53. What Mormon is past president of the International Society for Psychotherapy Research?

54. In what state or country did Butch Cassidy die?

55. Where did rugby champion Sid Going play for the great team called the All Blacks?

56. What world association was Jerrold R. Poth of Seattle named president of in 1974?

57. Where did Hugh Nibley do his undergraduate studies?

58. Who wrote *How to Prosper During the Coming Bad Years?*

59. As a boy, Neal Maxwell earned over ninety 4-H ribbons for raising what kind of animals?

60. In what city did President Kimball have surgery on his throat?

61. Who was the first woman athlete from BYU to win All-American honors four years in a row?

62. What General Authority wrote *A Plea for America?*

63. Arthur Salzner Anderson was the first man to hold what church position?

64. What honor for mothers did Catherine Peterson win in 1983?

65. Who dedicated the $3 million Osmond studio in Orem, Utah?

66. What position was homebuilder Eugene A. Gulledge named to by President Richard Nixon in 1969?

67. Who was elected chairman of the board of the Public Broadcasting Service in early 1980?

68. What national pageant did Janet Daines nearly win in 1973?

69. Who won the U.S. Amateur Golf Championship in 1977, joining such previous winners as Arnold Palmer and Jack Nicklaus?

47. Diving (*CA*, 1985, p. 314)

48. Twenty-six years (*CN*, 4/6/68, p. 13)

49. *The Personal Writings of Joseph Smith*

50. They were watching conference on television (*CN*, 10/28/78, p. 4)

51. To serve again as mission president (Ireland Dublin Mission) (*CN*, 3/22/80, p. 4)

52. Secretary of the Treasury (*CN*, 12/14/68, p. 4)

53. Allen Bergin (*EN*, 9/83, p. 34)

54. Washington state (*ABM*, p. 66)

55. New Zealand (and Going is white!) (*MA*, p. 22)

56. World Association of Detectives (*CA*, 1975, p. A21)

57. UCLA (*NTT*, p. xxii)

58. Howard Ruff (*TP*, Con. 1982, p. 18)

59. Pigs (*EN*, 2/82, p. 8)

60. New York City

61. Swimmer Lelei Fonoimoana (*MA II*, p. 121)

62. Ezra Taft Benson

63. Regional Representative (*CA*, 1976, p. D30)

64. National Young Mother of the Year (*TP*, 2/84, p. 56)

65. President Spencer W. Kimball (*CN*, 11/5/77, p. 4)

66. Commissioner of the Federal Housing Administration (FHA) (*CN*, 9/27/69, p. 3)

67. Dallin H. Oaks (*BYU*, 3/80, p. 5)

68. Miss Teenage America — she was named first alternate (*CA*, 1975, p. A13)

69. John Fought (*MA*, p. 98)

70. Where did Carlos Asay play college basketball?

71. In 1977, wheelchair athletes Mike Johnson and Curt Brinkman completed a record 115-mile marathon around the shoreline of what lake?

72. Why did All-American Eldon Fortie sign with the Canadian Football League rather than the NFL or the AFL?

73. Where did Danny White play college football?

74. How many baseball players hit more career home runs than Harmon Killebrew?

75. When Creed Haymond set the world record for the 220-yard dash, it stood for thirty-six years. What famous black runner finally broke it?

76. Who did *Golf Digest* name the number one amateur for 1977?

77. What team did Danny Ainge play professional baseball for?

78. Who defeated Sugar Ray Robinson to win the world middleweight boxing championship?

79. How many first-team All-America teams was Danny Ainge named to?

80. What prestigious baseball award did Vernon Law win in 1960?

81. Who came in before the first runner at the 1980 *Deseret News* Marathon?

82. What university president was the chairman of the U.S. National Commission on Excellence in Education, organized in the early 1980s?

83. In the early 1900s, Olympic gold medalist Alma Richards turned down $1,000 to do what?

84. What is the profession of Dorothy Carson, who was named 1979-80 American Business Woman of the Year?

85. Helvecio Martins was the first black man to serve in a stake presidency. His eldest son Marcus was the first black to do what?

86. Under Karl Tucker's leadership, how often was the BYU golf team ranked in the nation's top ten during the 1970s?

87. Which General Authority wrote a book about the Osmond family?

88. O. Leslie Stone was once vice president of what grocery store chain?

89. Who is president of the largest university system in the world?

70. University of Utah (*CN*, 3/1/80, p. 4)

71. Utah Lake (*MA*, p. 44)

72. He didn't want to play on Sunday (*MA II*, p. 151)

73. Arizona State University (*MA II*, p. 1)

74. Only four (*MA II*, p. 75)

75. Jessie Owens (*MA*, p. 2)

76. John Fought (*MA*, p. 97)

77. Toronto Blue Jays (*MA*, p. 69)

78. Gene Fullmer (*WW*, p. 12)

79. Five (*BYU*, 4/81, p. 18)

80. Cy Young Award (*WW*, p. 199)

81. Wheelchair competitor Curt Brinkman, beating runner Demetrio Cabanillas by ten minutes (*BYU*, 9/80, p. 13)

82. David Gardner (*TP*, 2/84, p. 40)

83. Allow a tobacco company to use his name in advertisements (*MA*, p. 9)

84. She is a judge (*CN*, 11/10/79, p. 11)

85. Serve a full-time mission (*CN*, 12/16/78, p. 7)

86. Nine times in ten years (*GMBYUS*, p. 45)

87. Paul H. Dunn (*CN*, 11/5/77, p. 4)

88. Safeway (*MMZ*, p. 363)

89. David Gardner, president of nine major campuses and five medical schools in the University of California system (*TP*, 2/84, p. 40)

90. Which Mormon philosopher wrote *Eternal Man?*

91. Who was named Church archivist in 1972?

92. Rex Lee was Assistant Attorney General under which U.S. President?

93. What General Authority was once incarcerated in a U.S. prisoner-of-war camp?

94. What golfer was named PGA Player of the Year in 1974?

95. Where did Roger Porter work in the early 1980s?

96. Who is the long-time track coach at BYU?

97. Spencer W. Kimball and Camilla Kimball first met at what event?

98. When Elder Teddy E. Brewerton won the highest honor given a pharmacist (The *Bowl of Hygeia*), what weekly news magazine published an article about it?

99. What sports championship did Jan Bucher win in 1979?

100. In 1981, Richard Richards was named national chairman for which political party?

101. Who was the founding managing editor of the *Ensign?*

102. What professional baseball team did Vernon Law play for?

103. Within two years, how old was President Kimball when he started to keep a journal?

104. What did Alma Richards do just before his winning high jump at the 1912 Olympics at Stockholm?

105. Who set an American indoor record for the two-mile run in 1981?

106. Who was the first major league baseball player to be selected to the all-star team at three different positions?

107. Budd Shields was an All-American in what sport in 1928?

108. Who was three-time winner of the Saddle Bronc World Championships?

109. What high school player was named *National Prep* Magazine's 1976 Junior of the Year in basketball?

110. Who was the number one gymnast in the United States in 1976?

111. What two athletes did Gordon B. Hinckley introduce to the priesthood session of the October 1984 general conference?

112. Ken Shelley made the Olympics in what sport?

113. Who was the head track coach at BYU from 1949 to the 1980s?

114. Who signed a $40 million football contract in the early 1980s?

90. Truman G. Madsen

91. Earl Olson (*CA*, 1975,
    p. A29)

92. President Gerald R. Ford
    (*CA*, 1982, p. 300)

93. F. Enzio Busche

94. Johnny Miller (*MA II*, p. 52)

95. The White House (*TP*,
    Jun./Jul. 1983, p. 31)

96. Clarence Robison (*BYU*,
    4/77, p. 21)

97. A dance (*SWK*, p. 83)

98. *Time* (*CN*, 11/4/78, p. 6)

99. World freestyle skiing (*MA*,
    p. 52)

100. The Republican Party (*CN*,
     2/21/81, p. 10)

101. Dallas Burnett

102. Pittsburgh Pirates (*MA II*,
     p. 90)

103. Ten years old (*CN*, 4/15/78,
     p. 3)

104. He knelt on the field and
     prayed (*MA*, p. 8)

105. Doug Padilla (*MA II*, p. 19)

106. Harmon Killebrew (*MA II*,
     p. 74)

107. Swimming (*MA*, p. 11)

108. Shawn Davis (*MA*, p. 18)

109. Danny Vranes (*MA* II, p. 8)

110. Wayne Young (*MA*, p. 91)

111. Peter Vidmar and Dale
     Murphy (*EN*, 11/84, p. 34)

112. Figure skating (*MA II*, p. 69)

113. Clarence Robinson (*MA II*,
     p. 223)

114. Steve Young

115. What member of the Quorum of the Twelve Apostles had grandfathers on both sides who were also Apostles?

116. Who served as personal secretary to Joseph Fielding Smith, Harold B. Lee, and Spencer W. Kimball?

117. How successful has Paul Robinson's *Fundamentals of Experimental Psychology* been?

118. Who became president of American Motors in 1954?

119. What future General Authority was named the outstanding young man in Salt Lake City in 1952?

120. In 1956, *Time* magazine noted that auto racer Ab Jenkins held more records in what category than any other person?

121. Which current General Authority was serving as a Sunday School teacher at the time of his call?

122. What did President Romney say is his "bread and butter"?

123. LaVern Watts Parmley was the president of what Church auxiliary from 1951 to 1974?

124. Who was the United States national men's figure skating champion in 1972?

125. Who co-edited the *Handbook of Psychotherapy and Behavior Change*, a standard reference in clinical psychology?

126. Who ordained Boyd K. Packer an Apostle?

127. What honor was athlete Neil Roberts given in 1963?

128. Bishop David J. Rollins was a prisoner of war in what country?

129. Who was the first surgeon ever to implant an artificial heart?

130. Who was the founding managing editor of the *Friend?*

131. Who was a banking executive in South America before his call as a General Authority?

132. What cabinet position did George Romney hold?

133. In 1968, *Swimming World* named Keith Russell the best in the world in what event?

134. Who was BYU's first consensus All-American quarterback?

135. What was Harmon Killebrew's personal record for most home runs in one game?

136. Name the two books Robert Allen had simultaneously on the *New York Times* best-seller list in 1983.

115. M. Russell Ballard (his grandfathers were Melvin J. Ballard and Hyrum Mack Smith)

116. D. Arthur Haycock (*EN*, 8/84, p. 25)

117. It is the best-selling text in its field, used in more than three hundred universities (*BYU*, 3/77, p. 3)

118. George Romney (*WW*, p. 138)

119. J. Thomas Fyans (*MMZ*, p. 368)

120. Distance speed racing (*MA II*, p. 80)

121. Ronald E. Poelman (*CA*, 1982, p. 90)

122. The scriptures (*CN*, 9/24/77, p. 13)

123. Primary (*CA*, 1980, p. 266)

124. Ken Shelley (*MA II*, p. 69)

125. Allen Bergin (*EN*, 9/83, p. 36)

126. Joseph Fielding Smith (*CA*, 1976, p. B53)

127. He was named *Sports Illustrated* High School Athlete of the Year (*MA II*, p. 154)

128. North Vietnam (*CN*, 2/17/79, p. 10)

129. Dr. William DeVries (*TP*, Feb./Mar. 1985, p. 33)

130. Lucile C. Reading

131. Robert E. Wells (*CA*, 1982, p. 87)

132. Secretary for Housing and Urban Development (*WW*, p. 124)

133. Diving (*MA*, p. 106)

134. Marc Wilson (*MA*, p. 122)

135. Three (*MA II*, p. 74)

136. *Nothing Down* and *Creating Wealth* (*TP*, 2/84, p. 63)

137. What future Apostle and his wife won the all-Church mixed-doubles tennis championship?

138. What Church athletic program did Homer Warner establish?

139. Who was the leading college freshman basketball scorer in 1978?

140. What position does baseball star Dale Murphy play?

141. In how many Olympics has Kresimir Cosic won a medal?

142. In 1980, Jan Shelley was ranked number one in the United States by the National Statistical Service for what sport?

143. What fictional character did *Sports Illustrated* compare BYU athlete Marc Wilson to?

144. What baseball player was Paul H. Dunn's boyhood idol?

145. The ambassador of what country made an unprecedented visit to Salt Lake City in January 1981?

146. Bruno Gerzeli was a star in what sport?

147. What do Mel Olsen, Roger French, Garth Hall, and Norm Chow have in common?

148. Who won the World Cup in Women's Freestyle Ballet Skiing in 1979 and 1980?

149. Elder Richard G. Scott is a prominent mechanical engineer and a specialist in what field of science?

150. Within three, how many times was Alf Engen a national ski champion?

151. Keith F. Nyborg was named U.S. Ambassador to Finland by what president?

152. What gave inventor Philo Farnsworth the idea of "scanning," making a television picture with a series of horizontal lines?

153. In 1974, Lorie Watson became national women's champion in what sport?

154. A twelve-story classroom office building was constructed on the BYU campus in 1980. What general authority is it named after?

155. What book did award-winning Merlo Pusey write about Dwight D. Eisenhower?

156. What honor did BYU's homecoming queen of 1947, Colleen Kay Hutchins, win in 1952?

157. Before his call as a General Authority, Joseph Anderson had a longer and closer association with different Presidents of the Church than almost anyone else. Why?

158. Who has repeatedly appeared on the *Today Show* to explain outdoor cooking techniques?

137. Marvin J. and Norma
     Ashton (*MMZ*, p. 295)

138. M-Men basketball (*MA II*,
     p. 211)

139. Danny Ainge (*BYU*, 3/78,
     p. 18)

140. Center field

141. Four—silver in 1968,
     bronze in 1972, silver in
     1976, and gold in 1980
     (*MA*, p. 30)

142. Gymnastics (*BYU*, 3/80,
     p. 21)

143. Ichabod Crane (*MA*, p. 124)

144. Lou Gehrig

145. China (*CA*, 1982, p. 17)

146. Soccer (*WW*, p. 152)

147. All were assistant coaches
     to BYU's LaVell Edwards at
     the same time (*BYU*, 9/90,
     p. 18)

148. Jan Bucher (*MA*, p. 53)

149. Nuclear energy (*CN*,
     4/30/77, p. 7)

150. Sixteen (*MA II*, p. 99)

151. Ronald Reagan (*CA*, 1982,
     p. 250)

152. Looking at rows of crops on
     an Idaho farm (*BYU*, 12/83,
     p. 43)

153. Motocross (*MA*, p. 39)

154. Spencer W. Kimball (*CN*,
     2/16/80, p. 10)

155. *Eisenhower, The President*
     (*D*, Spring 1977, p. 79)

156. Miss America

157. He was secretary to the
     First Presidency (*CN*,
     10/18/80, p. 4)

158. Dian Thomas (*TP*, Jun./Jul.
     1983, p. 20)

159. Who was the first General Authority called from Germany?

160. What is President Kimball's favorite hymn?

161. Who wrote *Prophecy, Key to the Future?*

162. What instrument does Elder Russell M. Nelson like to play each morning?

163. Neil D. Schaerrer was the president of what Church auxiliary from 1977 to 1979?

164. Budd Shields broke one of the swimming records of which famous swimmer and actor in 1927?

165. What monarch requested an original cartoon from Steve Benson?

166. Who was BYU's first bona-fide first-team All-American quarterback?

167. During his presidency at BYU, Dallin H. Oaks taught one course per year in what subject?

168. When steeplechase runner Henry Marsh fell into a fish pond at age two, who found him floating face down in the water?

169. What Marine was sent back to the ship to obtain the flag used in the historic flag-raising on Iwo Jima?

170. What was the subject of Paul H. Dunn's *The Ten Most Wanted Men?*

171. In 1952, Mel Hutchins was Rookie of the Year in what professional sport?

172. In 1976, who became golf's youngest millionaire?

173. Who won a gold medal in the high jump in the 1912 Olympics?

174. Who set an NCAA single-game high in passing in 1976?

175. In 1983, Larry Nielson became the first American to do what without the help of supplemental oxygen?

176. Jay Silvester set a world record in what track-and-field event?

177. What prominent athlete was born in Payette, Idaho?

178. What is the family relationship between basketball players Jeff Judkins and Danny Vranes?

179. What sport did Jay Don Blake win an NCAA championship in?

180. What national council has Wesley Burr served as president of?

181. What huge conglomerate does Nolan Archibald serve as chief operating officer of?

182. What General Authority was once a director of the Union Pacific Railroad, *Deseret News*, and Intermountain Health Care?

159. F. Enzio Busche (*CA*, 1982, p. 88)

160. "I Need Thee Every Hour" (*CN*, 1/6/79, p. 10)

161. Duane Crowther

162. Organ (*EN*, 6/84, p. 13)

163. Young Men (*CA*, 1980, p. 267)

164. Johnny Weismuller — Shields beat his time in the 220-freestyle swim (*MA*, p. 15)

165. Queen Elizabeth (*TP*, 2/84, p. 55)

166. Eldon Fortie (*MA II*, p. 148)

167. Law (*CN*, 5/17/80, p. 8)

168. His grandfather, Henry D. Moyle (*MA*, pp. 56–57)

169. A. Theodore Tuttle (*MMZ*, p. 457)

170. Leadership

171. Basketball (*MA II*, p. 135)

172. Johnny Miller (*MA II*, p. 52)

173. Alma Richards (*MA*, p. 6)

174. Gifford Nielsen — his passing yardage was 468, against Utah State (*MA*, p. 34)

175. Climb Mt. Everest — only three other men in history have matched that feat (*TP*, 2/84, p. 31)

176. Discus (*MA*, p. 84)

177. Harmon Killebrew (*WW*, p. 119)

178. Cousins

179. Golf (*CA*, 1982, p. 253)

180. National Council on Family Relations (*CA*, 1983, p. 249)

181. Beatrice Foods Company (*TP*, 2/84, p. 21)

182. Dallin H. Oaks (*CN*, 5/17/80, p. 9)

People

183. What baseball hall of famer was Paul H. Dunn's childhood idol?

184. Steve Benson won a 1984 award for what area of journalism?

185. Who was the NBA number one draft choice in 1951?

186. What body-building title did Larry Scott win in 1964?

187. What popular Mormon biographer has written at least five biographies of Presidents of the Church?

188. The work at what famous research laboratory was directed by Dr. Harvey Fletcher?

189. What was Elder Spencer W. Kimball's first book?

190. Within five, how many passes in a row did Steve Young complete to set a national collegiate record?

191. Who was a supermarket executive before his call to the Presiding Bishopric?

192. What was the title of the popular Afton Day book about being a wife?

193. What year did Dian Thomas's book *Roughing It Easy* make the *New York Times* bestseller list?

194. When Elder Boyd K. Packer served his country in the Pacific during World War II, what was his assignment?

195. David B. Haight served two terms as mayor of what California city?

196. Who spent thirty-two years as a Catholic priest before converting to the Church and joining the BYU faculty?

197. Who wrote a small book called *Marriage?*

198. Who was given the 1979-80 National Player of the Year Award by the American Women Sports Foundation?

199. Larry Scott became a champion in what sport?

200. Why did the Saints know the name of Sister Marianne Clark Sharp in the early 1970s?

201. What two Utah collegiate basketball players were dubbed by *Sports Illustrated* as "a double Danny dandy"?

202. Dr. Harvey Fletcher is known as the father of what kind of sound?

203. Because his father was a mission president, where did Robert L. Backman attend high school?

204. Which Apostle has the middle name Bitner?

205. How many members of the Church were seated in Congress after the 1982 election—eight, ten, twelve, or fourteen?

183. Lou Gehrig (*CN*, 3/17/79, p. 10)

184. Editorial cartoons (*CA*, 1985, p. 309)

185. Mel Hutchins (*MA II*, p. 135)

186. Mr. Universe (*MA*, p. 119)

187. Francis M. Gibbons

188. Bell Telephone Laboratory (*BYU*, 9/80, p. 3)

189. *The Miracle of Forgiveness*

190. Twenty-two (*GMBYUS*, p. 161)

191. Vaughn J. Featherstone (*MMZ*, p. 519)

192. *How to Be a Perfect Wife and Other Myths*

193. 1975 (*CA*, 1978, p. 15)

194. He was a bomber pilot (*CN*, 4/28/79, p. 2)

195. Palo Alto (*CA*, 1982, p. 78)

196. John Staley (*TP*, Con. 82, p. 15)

197. Spencer W. Kimball

198. BYU basketballer Tina Gunn (*MA II*, p. 34)

199. Body building (*MA*, p. 118)

200. She was one of Belle Spafford's last two counselors (*CA*, 1975, p. A12)

201. Danny Vranes and Danny Ainge (*MA II*, p. 9)

202. Stereophonic (*CN*, 5/5/79, p. 11)

203. Capetown, South Africa (*CN*, 4/29/78, p. 4)

204. Gordon B. Hinckley (*MMZ*, p. 287)

205. Twelve (*TP*, 3/83, p. 60)

206. Who was the first golfer to win over $200,000 on the PGA tour in one year?

207. What quarterback was the first-round draft pick of the Oakland Raiders in 1980?

208. Alma Richards won three national AAU championships in three track and field events. Name them.

209. What General Authority gave Henry Marsh a priesthood blessing shortly before he went to the 1976 Montreal Olympics?

210. What prominent athlete did professional baseball player Barry Bonnell baptize?

211. Most of the Presidents of the Church were in what decade of their lives when they died?

212. What Church member was elected to baseball's Hall of Fame in 1984?

213. Where did LaVell Edwards play college football?

214. Who set an American record in the steeplechase run?

215. Where does Angela M. Buchanan's signature commonly appear?

216. What position was Ruth Funk appointed to in 1972?

217. What position was Keith Wilcox called to in 1984?

218. Who was named to the Board of International Broadcasting in 1983, serving with author James Michener and AFL-CIO president Lane Kirkland?

219. Who coauthored the book *Marriage and Family: Gospel Insights?*

220. What prominent businessman was chairman of all the inaugural activities for President Richard Nixon in 1969?

221. In what country was Hartman Rector, Jr., baptized?

222. In 1976, Henry Isaksen was elected president of what Mormon association?

223. Where was Elder F. Enzio Busche living at the time of his call to the First Quorum of the Seventy in 1977?

224. After winning the World Series in 1960, why was Vernon Law sent back to the minors in 1962?

225. Who was named head of Church Public Communications in 1972?

226. Sam Cowley, a member of the Church and an FBI agent, was killed in a shootout with what notorious criminal?

227. Linn Rockwood won the national championship in what sport in 1957?

206. Billy Casper (*MA II*, p. 272)

207. Marc Wilson (*MA*, p. 129)

208. High jump (1913), decath-
alon (1915), and shot put
(1918) (*MA*, p. 9)

209. President Marion G.
Romney (*MA*, p. 61)

210. Dale Murphy (*MA II*, p. 117)

211. Their eighties

212. Harmon Killebrew (*TP*,
Feb./Mar. 1985, p. 30)

213. Utah State University
(*MA II*, p. 243)

214. Henry Marsh

215. On U.S. dollar bills (*TP*,
10/84, p. 39)

216. General president of the
Young Women (*RS*, p. 95)

217. Member of the First
Quorum of the Seventy (*EN*,
11/84, p. 34)

218. Arch Madsen (*TP*, 2/84,
p. 39)

219. Stephen R. Covey and
Truman Madsen

220. J. Willard Marriott (*CN*,
1/11/69, p. 3)

221. Japan (*MMZ*, p. 462)

222. Association of Mormon
Counselors and Psycho-
therapists (*CA*, 1978, p. 19)

223. Germany (*CN*, 10/22/77,
p. 5)

224. He suffered an injury that
affected his game (*MA II*,
p. 92)

225. Wendell J. Ashton (*CA*,
1975, p. F3)

226. Baby Face Nelson

227. Tennis — both singles and
doubles (*MA II*, p. 107)

228. What scientist contributed to the success of Pioneer 10, the space shuttle, and the artificial heart?

229. What investigative reporter has won a Pulitzer Prize?

230. What Apostle appeared on the *Today Show* in April 1980?

231. Within two years, how old was Thomas S. Monson when he was called to preside as bishop over a ward of more than twelve hundred people?

232. Where was 1985 Miss America Sharlene Wells born?

233. What magazine dubbed Jim Jenson with the name "Dinosaur Jim"?

234. What General Authority wrote the book entitled *The Human Touch?*

235. Who was BYU's first All-American golfer?

236. Who was Marion Isabell Smith?

237. Jack Carlson was chief economist and vice president of what national business organization?

238. What Apostle wrote *The Holy Temple?*

239. In 1923, George Nelson was world light-heavyweight champion in what sport?

240. Within ten thousand, how many full-time students attend the University of California system, presided over by David Gardner?

241. Where did Merlin Olsen play college football?

242. Name one of two distant cousins to President Kimball who ran unsuccessfully for U.S. president in the 1960s.

243. Who was named by the International Diving Federation in 1967 as the top springboard diver in the world?

244. Who was NBA Coach of the Year in 1971?

245. What world champion track star refused his coach's invitation to drink wine?

246. What wheelchair racing event did Curtis Brinkman win in 1980?

247. Who was quarterback of the BYU football team in 1973-74?

248. Ivy Baker Priest was the first member of the Church to hold what political position?

249. What future Apostle served in the mission field under Hugh B. Brown?

250. How did Karl Tucker's BYU golf team fare in the 1981 NCAA national tournament?

228. James Fletcher (*EN*, 4/84, p. 26)

229. Jack Anderson (*CA*, 1980, p. 12)

230. Gordon B. Hinckley (*CA*, 1981, p. 27)

231. Twenty-two years old (*CN*, 12/27/80, p. 7)

232. Paraguay (*BYU*, 12/84, p. 11)

233. *Reader's Digest* (*BYU*, 12/83, p. 16)

234. Paul H. Dunn

235. Johnny Miller (*MA II*, p. 52)

236. The maiden name of Belle Smith Spafford, general president of the Relief Society in the 1950s and 1960s (*EN*, 4/82, p. 80)

237. U.S. Chamber of Commerce (*CA*, 1980, p. 270)

238. Boyd K. Packer

239. Wrestling (*MA II*, p. 228)

240. 150,000 (*TP*, 2/84, p. 40)

241. Utah State University (*MA II*, p. 45)

242. Hubert Humphrey, Nelson Rockefeller (*NS*, pp. 30, 64)

243. Keith Russell (*MA*, p. 106)

244. Dick Motta — coach of the Chicago Bulls (*MA II*, p. 195)

245. Creed Haymond (*IS*, p. 125)

246. Boston Marathon (*MA II*, p. 40)

247. Gary Sheide

248. United States Treasurer (*CA*, 1982, p. 20)

249. Marvin J. Ashton

250. They won the national championship (*GMBYUS*, p. 64)

251. Who was the editor of the *New Era* beginning in 1972?

252. In what country was Camilla Kimball born?

253. Who was the first Mormon woman elected to the United States Senate?

254. What general president of the Young Women was elected vice president of the National Council of Women in April 1982?

255. Who was editor of the 1978 edition of a 703-page textbook, *Cases and Text on the Law of Trusts?*

256. What future General Authority served aboard a submarine chaser in the Pacific during World War II?

257. What Mormon has served as U.S. Ambassador to the North Atlantic Treaty Organization in Europe?

258. Who motivated noted scientist Henry Eyring to go to college?

259. What General Authority played baseball for the St. Louis Cardinals?

260. Who was the first occupant of the Richard L. Evans Chair of Christian Understanding at BYU?

261. Alma Richards repeatedly met the great Jim Thorpe in track meets after the 1912 Olympics. How many times did Richards beat Thorpe?

262. What cabinet post did T.H. Bell hold?

263. Who wrote *The Message of the Joseph Smith Papyri?*

264. In thirty-three years of coaching track at BYU, how many times has Clarence Robison taken his team into the top ten?

265. What outlaw promised to stop robbing banks in Wyoming and kept his word?

266. How did Tina Gunn distinguish herself in sports in 1980?

267. What national honor did Joan Fisher receive in 1968?

268. W. Jay Eldredge was the president of what Church auxiliary in 1972?

269. Why was Marc Wilson unable to finish his senior year of high school football?

270. Who wrote *One Silent Sleepless Night?*

271. Who made the stunning winning basket in the BYU-Notre Dame game in the 1981 NCAA tournament?

272. What prominent Book of Mormon scholar authored the *Book of Mormon Compendium?*

273. Champion wrestler Mike Young was also a state champion in what other sport?

251. Brian Kelly

252. Mexico (*CN*, 1/6/79, p. 6)

253. Paula Hawkins of Florida (*CN*, 11/15/80, p. 5)

254. Elaine Cannon (*TP*, 3/83, p. 55)

255. Dallin H. Oaks (*BYU*, 3/78, p. 13)

256. Marion D. Hanks (*OSGA*, p. 96)

257. David M. Kennedy (*EN*, 5/83, p. 89)

258. His sister, Camilla Eyring Kimball (*TP*, 2/84, p. 18)

259. Paul H. Dunn

260. Truman Madsen (*CA*, 1974, p. 62)

261. Every time (*MA*, p. 9)

262. Secretary of Education (*CA*, 1982, p. 17)

263. Hugh Nibley

264. Twenty (*MA II*, p. 223)

265. Butch Cassidy (*ABM*, p. 63)

266. She was the nation's leading female basketball scorer with thirty-one points per game (*BYU*, 6/80, p. 19)

267. Mrs. America (*CN*, 10/5/68, p. 3)

268. YMMIA (*CA*, 1980, p. 267)

269. He broke his jaw (*MA*, p. 122)

270. Spencer W. Kimball

271. Danny Ainge (*GMBYUS*, p. 40)

272. Sidney B. Sperry

273. Boxing (*MA II*, p. 144)

274. Who became head coach of the Detroit Lions in 1977?

275. When Budd Shields set a new national record in the 440-yard freestyle swim in 1928, how many seconds did he shave off the old record?

276. Within ten, how many tons of dinosaur fossils did Jim Jenson dig up in his career?

277. Who set a world record in the 220-yard dash in 1919?

278. Who was college football coach of the year in 1984?

279. Who was the first professional golfer to visit American troops in Vietnam?

280. How many Presidents of the Church were six feet tall or taller?

281. What sport did Gifford Nielsen choose to concentrate on in his sophomore year at BYU?

282. President Max W. Woodbury set a record for service (fifty years) as president of a branch of what group of handicapped people?

283. In 1979, Vona R. Houtz was elected president of the National Auxiliary to the Veterans of Foreign Wars. Within fifty thousand, how many people did she preside over?

284. Who has been president of both the University of Utah and the University of California?

285. Until 1977 Sterling W. Sill was commentator for nearly nine hundred inspirational messages on what long-running syndicated radio series?

286. What did Andrew K. Watt, an advanced-design engineer for Oldsmobile Motor Company, help develop in American cars?

287. What great-grandson of Parley P. Pratt was a prominent politician?

288. Who did *Sports Illustrated* call in 1982 "the best indoor distance runner the U.S. has ever produced"?

289. In 1985, Anthony Burns became chairman of the board for what company?

290. In what year was Jeffrey Holland named president of BYU?

291. What was the relationship of the composer and the author of "A Voice Hath Spoken," J. Marinus Jensen and J.J. Keeler?

292. How many years did Ezra Taft Benson serve in the U.S. cabinet?

293. Who founded a $3 billion a year hotel and restaurant business?

274. Tommy Hudspeth (*BYU*, 3/77, p. 11)

275. Fifteen (*MA*, p. 12)

276. One hundred tons (*BYU*, 12/83, p. 15)

277. Creed Haymond (*MA*, p. 1)

278. LaVell Edwards

279. Billy Casper (*MA II*, p. 278)

280. Four—Joseph Smith, Heber J. Grant, George Albert Smith, David O. McKay (*CA*, 1982, pp. 97—102)

281. Basketball—he didn't play football at all that year (*MA*, p. 33)

282. The deaf (Ogden LDS Deaf Branch) (*CN*, 2/4/67, p. 10)

283. 626,000 (*CA*, 1980, p. 271)

284. David Gardner

285. "Sunday Evening from Temple Square" (*CN*, 7/2/77, p. 6)

286. Front-wheel drive (*CN*, 10/14/67, p. 7)

287. George Romney (*WW*, p. 134)

288. Doug Padilla (*MA II*, p. 25)

289. Ryder (*DN*, 4/3/85, B5)

290. 1980 (*EN*, 7/80, p. 75)

291. Grandfather and grandson (*SMH*, p. 281)

292. Eight (*CA*, 1985, p. 97)

293. J. Willard Marriott

294. In 1979, Jack Carlson was named vice president of what is reputedly the largest trade organization in the world. What is it?

295. Erroll Bennett is a soccer star from what country?

296. What Apostle wrote the book *Pathways to Perfection?*

297. Who was named Church Historian in 1972?

298. Who is the only leader to go from staff member at Church headquarters to membership in the First Presidency?

299. Who was the first non-American college basketball player to win All-American honors?

300. Who was the NCAA All-Around Gymnastics Champion in 1975?

Simpler Questions for Use as Needed

301. What is President Hinckley's middle initial?

302. How old was Jamie Smith when he won the "Boys Twelve and Under World Rodeo Championship"?

303. What sport was young Spencer W. Kimball referring to when he said, "I would rather play this game than eat"?

304. True or false: Johnny Miller once won $500,000 in a golf tournament.

305. Was President Spencer W. Kimball raised in Utah, Idaho, or Arizona?

306. True or false: Larry Scott was Mr. America and Mr. Universe.

307. True or false: A Church member owns the Utah Jazz basketball team.

308. True or false: A Church member was killed for opposing Hitler.

309. True or false: A Church member wrote most of the songs on Michael Jackson's *Thriller* album.

310. True or false: Henry Marsh was a diver in the 1984 Olympics.

311. True or false: President Kimball was an Apostle for sixty years before he became President of the Church.

312. True or false: Elder Paul H. Dunn once played professional baseball.

313. How old was Melinda Bassett when she beat fifteen thousand other students in a spelling bee in Europe?

314. True or false: A Church member invented the TV.

315. True or false: Gordon B. Hinckley was a paper boy when he was young.

294. The National Association of
     Realtors (*CA*, 1980, p. 270)

295. Tahiti (*EN*, 10/82, p. 15)

296. Thomas S. Monson (*CA*,
     1975, p. A14)

297. Leonard Arrington (*CA*,
     1975, p. F2)

298. Gordon B. Hinckley (*EN*,
     1/82, p. 13)

299. Kresimir Cosic (*MA*, p. 28)

300. Wayne Young (*MA*, p. 93)

301. B

302. Nine

303. Basketball (*CN*, 8/30/80,
     p. 13)

304. True

305. Arizona

306. True

307. True

308. True

309. False

310. False — he ran in the
     steeplechase

311. False

312. True

313. Ten

314. True (Philo Farnsworth)

315. True

316. Is Gene Fullmer famous for boxing, car racing, or painting?

317. What is President Kimball's middle initial?

318. Malo Weeks, 15, received an award for saving his brother and a friend from drowning. What ocean were they in?

319. True or false: Camilla Kimball's brother was a famous scientist.

320. Where was President Spencer W. Kimball's wife, Camilla, born? Was she born in England, Canada, Mexico, or the United States?

321. Is General Authority Yoshihiko Kikuchi from China, Japan, Korea, or Taiwan?

322. Is George Romney famous for running for U.S. president or for inventing the radio?

323. What professional sport do Johnny Miller and Billy Casper play — hockey, basketball, or golf?

324. True or false: Former Miss America Sharlene Wells lived for several years in South America.

325. True or false: Dallin Oaks was on the Utah Supreme Court before he became an Apostle.

326. Was President Spencer W. Kimball ever a bishop?

327. How many General Authorities since 1965 have had beards?

328. True or false: George Albert Smith was President of the Church when general conference was first broadcast on television.

329. True or false: Vice President George Bush is a member of the Church.

330. True or false: Henry Marsh, Paul Cummings, and Wade Bell are famous runners.

331. Which of these General Authorities is an American Indian — Charles Didier, Rex D. Pinegar, or George P. Lee?

332. Is Danc Iorg a professional baseball player or a country-western singer?

333. Brian Benson, 8, won a national poster contest sponsored by what breakfast cereal company?

334. What sport did Harmon Killebrew and Vernon Law play — football, baseball, or basketball?

335. What sport does Dale Murphy play — football, baseball, or soccer?

336. Did Mark Nash, 14, win a national contest in baton twirling, chess, or model building?

337. Did President Spencer W. Kimball learn to play the piano, the trumpet, or the guitar when he was a boy?

316. Boxing

317. W

318. Pacific

319. True

320. Mexico

321. Japan

322. Running for president

323. Golf

324. True

325. True

326. No

327. None

328. True

329. False

330. True

331. George P. Lee

332. Professional baseball player

333. Kellogg

334. Baseball

335. Baseball

336. Baton twirling

337. Piano

338. How old was Paul Ewing when he helped rescue a drowning man — nine, eleven, twenty, or ninety-five?

339. True or false: Barney Clark, the first man in history with an artificial heart, was a Mormon.

340. True or false: President Marion G. Romney was born in Mexico.

341. Was Joseph Fielding Smith a basketball, football, or baseball fan?

342. What position do Thomas S. Monson, Boyd K. Packer, and Dallin H. Oaks all hold?

343. True or false: A current member of the Quorum of the Twelve once performed open-heart surgery on President Kimball.

344. Was Wayne Young a star basketball player, gymnast, or runner?

345. True or false: A Church member invented stereo sound.

346. Has a Church Relief Society president ever been on the *Phil Donahue Show?*

347. Which of these men was never a counselor in the First Presidency — LeGrand Richards, N. Eldon Tanner, or Marion G. Romney?

348. True or false: Elder Ezra Taft Benson was an important government official under U.S. president Dwight D. Eisenhower.

349. True or false: A member of the Church has been heavyweight boxing champion of the world.

350. Was Russell Nelson a businessman, a lawyer, or a doctor before becoming an Apostle?

338. Eleven

339. True

340. True

341. Baseball

342. Apostle

343. True

344. Gymnast

345. True (Harvey Fletcher)

346. Yes (Barbara B. Smith)

347. LeGrand Richards

348. True

349. True (Jack Dempsey)

350. Doctor

PART **6** Arts and Entertainment

1. Which early Apostle wrote the words to "The Morning Breaks; the Shadows Flee"?

2. What choir did composer Charles J. Thomas lead?

3. What was the language in which "Silent Night" was originally written?

4. Name one of the two Zane Grey novels that were made into motion pictures in 1918, both of which had partial Mormon themes.

5. What song was the inspiration for "MIA, We Hail Thee"?

6. True or false: Rock singer Tina Turner has a sister who is a member of the Church.

7. Which hymn was sung by the passengers of the *Titanic* as it sank?

8. Which hymn was written by a Union soldier in the Civil War?

9. When the Tabernacle Choir made its first broadcast, where was the microphone placed?

10. What Church-supported musical was produced for the U.S. bicentennial celebration?

11. A cartoon in *The Lantern* (1852) had Brigham Young saying he had how many wives?

12. How does the second verse of "Come, Ye Disconsolate" begin?

13. Who was the first leader of the Tabernacle Choir?

14. What was the full name of hymn writer O.P. Huish?

15. What major event celebrating the arts is held annually at Brigham Young University?

16. What film about Deadwood Dick was released in 1915?

17. Within five, how many verses were originally included in "Jesus, the Very Thought of Thee"?

18. What humorous record album did Gordon Jump help create in 1982?

19. How did early recording engineers deaden the reverberations of sound in the Tabernacle?

20. What was Mormon fiction called beginning in the 1880s?

21. What was located across the street from the home of the boy who eventually built the original Tabernacle organ?

22. When sixty loudspeakers were purchased to help the Tabernacle Choir hear the organ better, where were they placed?

23. In the 1911 film *A Victim of the Mormons*, what is a pretty maiden forced to do?

1. Parley P. Pratt (*SMH,* p. 263)

2. The temple choir (*SMH,* p. 179)

3. German (*SMH,* p. 176)

4. *Riders of the Purple Sage* and *The Rainbow Trail* (*D,* Spring 1977, p. 63)

5. "Hail, B.Y., Hail" (*SMH,* p. 138)

6. True

7. "Nearer, My God, to Thee" (*SMH,* p. 128)

8. "God of Our Fathers, Whose Almighty Hand" (*SMH,* p. 63)

9. A boy stood on a stepladder, holding it at arm's length above his head (*CS,* p. 224)

10. *Threads of Glory* (*EN,* 7/77, p. 92)

11. One thousand (*MGI,* p. 19)

12. "Joy of the desolate" (*Hymns,* no. 18)

13. John Parry (*CS,* p. 6)

14. Orson Pratt Huish (*SMH,* p. 99)

15. The Mormon Arts Festival (*BP,* p. 405)

16. *Deadwood Dick Spoils Brigham Young* (*D,* Spring 1977, p. 61)

17. Forty-eight (*SMH,* p. 164)

18. *Latter-day Night Live* (*TP,* 3/83, p. 20)

19. They hung huge, heavy curtains across the entire interior, in front of the choir (*CS,* p. 200)

20. Home literature (*EN,* 6/81, p. 59)

21. An organ factory (*CS,* p. 20)

22. Under the choir seats (*CS,* p. 53)

23. Enter into a polygamous marriage (*D,* Spring 1977, p. 61)

24. Which hymn was written by a man who earlier had been a private secretary to Joseph Smith?

25. Who created the paintings now reproduced in some editions of the Book of Mormon?

26. In "Dear to the Heart of the Shepherd," where are the sheep wandering?

27. What language was "Praise to the Lord" originally written in?

28. Which composer had sixty-two hymns in *Latter-day Saint Hymns?*

29. What was the subject of an hour-long TV series pilot made for NBC in 1971?

30. In which section of the Doctrine and Covenants did the Lord command the Church to make a collection of hymns?

31. Which is the largest of the Church-commissioned sculptures?

32. Name one of the three temples LeConte Stewart painted murals in.

33. Virginia Sorensen's novel, *A Little Lower Than the Angels*, is set in what place?

34. In what decade was the Mormon Youth Symphony and Chorus organized?

35. In "Come, Come, Ye Saints," how are the Saints to wend their way?

36. Which hymn was written after the mobbing at Independence, Missouri?

37. What place is described in "Zion Stands with Hills Surrounded"?

38. Name one of the several television western series that have treated Mormons favorably.

39. Which hymn writer was Assistant Church Historian?

40. What was the hymn tune for "Glory to God on High" originally called?

41. What television series starring Robert Wagner did Glen Larson help produce?

42. When did H. H. Peterson, author of "There Is an Hour of Peace and Rest," write most of his songs?

43. What company made the first phonograph record of the Tabernacle Choir?

44. Name one of the three temples A. B. Wright painted murals in.

45. What movie did Doty-Dayton Productions make about orphaned children crossing the plains?

46. What five European languages did the Church broadcast over shortwave from New York from 1961 to 1974?

47. Who did Stewart Petersen portray in a 1976 Church film?

24. "Come, Come, Ye Saints," by William Clayton (*SMH*, p. 20)

25. Arnold Friberg (*TP*, 10/84, p. 47)

26. Out in the desert (*Hymns*, no. 26)

27. German (*SMH*, p. 166)

28. George Careless (*CS*, p. 353)

29. Contemporary Mormons (*D*, Spring 1977, p. 66)

30. Section 25 (*SMH*, p. xxi)

31. The Garden of Women at Nauvoo (*EN*, 7/77, p. 86)

32. Hawaii, Alberta, Arizona (*EN*, 7/77, p. 57)

33. Nauvoo (*BP*, p. 396)

34. The 1960s (*EN*, 7/77, p. 87)

35. With joy (*Hymns*, no. 13)

36. "Now Let Us Rejoice" (*SMH*, p. 124)

37. Probably Jerusalem (*SMH*, p. 219)

38. *Bonanza, The New Land, Big Valley, Here Come the Brides, Death Valley Days* (*D*, Spring 1977, p. 66)

39. John Jaques, author of "Oh Say, What Is Truth" (*SMH*, p. 152)

40. "Moscow" (*SMH*, p. 52)

41. *Switch*

42. Late at night, by candle-light (*SMH*, p. 132)

43. Columbia Phonograph Company of New York City (*CS*, p. 196)

44. Hawaii, Alberta, Arizona (*EN*, 7/77, p. 40)

45. *Seven Alone* (*D*, Spring 1977, p. 67)

46. English, Spanish, Portuguese, French, and German (*D*, Spring 1977, p. 31)

47. Joseph Smith (*CA*, 1977, p. 233)

48. What did two world travelers say of the Salt Lake Choir in the 1850s?

49. What is the musical *The Order Is Love* about?

50. Where was the tune to "Truth Reflects upon Our Senses" first published?

51. What 1976 Church television special did the Lennon Sisters appear in?

52. Why did Utah's Governor William Spry threaten to bar all motion pictures from the state in 1912?

53. What railroad sponsored a Tabernacle Choir trip to Idaho in 1939?

54. Who wrote the book *The Rummage Sale?*

55. After Evan Stephens was appointed Tabernacle Choir conductor in 1890, how many singers did he add to the choir?

56. Which popular Christmas hymn was written by a Church member?

57. What famous author visited a Mormon emigrant ship and came back with a favorable report?

58. What Mormon writer published the collection of short stories entitled *Under the Cottonwoods?*

59. Marilyn McMeen Brown's *The Earthkeepers* (1979) is a novel about the founding of which Utah community?

60. In "Come, Ye Thankful People," where are we to join in song?

61. In the William W. Phelps hymn rejoicing in our earthly home, how many flowers does earth have?

62. Who was executive producer of the anti-Mormon film *A Mormon Maid* in 1917?

63. Who was the playwright of *Saturday's Warrior?*

64. For what occasion did the Tabernacle Choir travel to New York in 1911?

65. What award-winning film was made in Germany in 1967 with Church cooperation?

66. Christian Jacobs played Sally Struthers's son in what short-lived television series?

67. "God of Power, God of Right" was written by what senator from Utah?

68. Which hymn was authored and composed by a missionary and his convert?

69. What popular children's book series was written by the author of *Papa Married a Mormon?*

70. How long was the Tabernacle Choir in existence before it held its first auditions?

48. Their singing was as good as that in Westminster Abbey (*EN*, 7/77, pp. 83–84)

49. The United Order (*BP*, p. 317)

50. A book called *Another Sheaf of White Spirituals* (*SMH*, p. 202)

51. *The Family . . . and Other Living Things* (*CA*, 1980, p. 17)

52. Viciously anti-Mormon films were being shown (*D*, Spring 1977, p. 61)

53. The Union Pacific Railroad (*CS*, p. 91)

54. Don Marshall (*BP*, p. 298)

55. One hundred (*CS*, p. 62)

56. "Far, Far Away on Judea's Plains" (*SMH*, p. 40)

57. Charles Dickens (*OHUM*, pp. 103–4)

58. Douglas H. Thayer

59. Provo (*EN*, 7/81, p. 60)

60. In the temple (*Hymns*, no. 29)

61. "Earth, with Her Ten Thousand Flowers" (*Hymns*, no. 30)

62. Cecil B. DeMille (*D*, Spring 1977, p. 59)

63. Doug Stewart (*EN*, 7/77, p. 86)

64. The National Irrigation Congress (*SMH*, p. 251)

65. *Mahlzeiten* (*D*, Spring 1977, p. 66)

66. *Gloria* (*TP*, 3/83, p. 65)

67. Wallace F. Bennett (*SMH*, p. 43)

68. "Oh Say, What Is Truth?" by John Jaques and Ellen Melling (*SMH*, p. 151)

69. The Great Brain books (*EN*, 7/81, p. 60)

70. Sixty-seven years (*CS*, p. 10)

71. What did a 1906 *Life* magazine cartoon have a Mormon say about a chorus line?

72. The earliest motion picture to touch on Mormon life was produced in 1905. What was it called?

73. When the song says, "For some must push and some must pull," what comes next?

74. What did commercials in *The Family . . . and Other Living Things* offer the viewer?

75. What were polysophical societies designed to do in nineteenth-century Utah?

76. Which hymn was written after the author was briefly lost at sea?

77. For what age group was "Onward, Christian Soldiers" originally written?

78. When the Tabernacle Choir first sang in Paris, all tickets were sold out two weeks in advance. What did the French do to cope with the disappointment?

79. What was the original name of *The Relief Society Magazine?*

80. In what decade did the Hill Cumorah Pageant begin?

81. What famous author said that if Mormonism could endure unchanged to the fourth generation, it would become the greatest power on earth?

82. At a Tabernacle Choir concert at Stanford University in 1902, what song most brought down the house?

83. In what periodical did "Redeemer of Israel," adapted by W. W. Phelps, first appear?

84. In the poem "Santa in Salt Lake," printed in a non-Mormon periodical in 1905, what did Santa find in a Salt Lake home?

85. Within three years, when did the Osmond Brothers first start performing together?

86. At what age was Alexander Schreiner made organist of his branch in Germany?

87. When was the choir first organized that eventually became known as the Tabernacle Choir?

88. What game did the Tabernacle Choir refuse to play on board ship as they traveled to Europe for the first time?

89. What was unique about the original LDS hymnbook, compared to those today?

90. What did Salt Lake City's reconstructed Wilkes Theater become?

91. What movie about Mormons was made in 1969 but never released?

92. In what year did *The Donny and Marie Show* begin its first full season on TV?

71. He was making arrange-
ments to marry them all
(*MGI*, p. 70)

72. *A Trip to Salt Lake City* (*D*,
Spring 1977, p. 61)

73. "As we go marching up the
hill"

74. An abbreviated copy of the
Family Home Evening man-
ual (*D*, Spring 1977, p. 33)

75. Promote cultural appreciation (*EN*, 7/77, p. 85)

76. "Lead, Kindly Light" (*SMH*,
p. 119)

77. Children (*SMH*, p. 133)

78. They broadcast the concert
over the entire French radio
network (*CS*, p. 135)

79. *Relief Society Bulletin* (*CA*,
1975, p. F29)

80. The 1930s (*EN*, 7/77, p. 86)

81. Leo Tolstoy (*NE*, 3/71,
p. 46)

82. Stanford's college song
(*CS*, p. 74)

83. *Evening and Morning Star*,
in 1832 (*SMH*, p. 206)

84. Sixty-three stockings hang-
ing from the mantle (*MGI*,
p. 70)

85. 1958 (*TP*, 2/84, p. 27)

86. Eight years old (*CN*,
12/10/77, p. 6)

87. 1849 (*CS*, p. 6)

88. Bingo (*CS*, p. 109)

89. It contained no music, only
"poems" (*CS*, p. 35)

90. The Promised Valley Play-
house (*D*, Spring 1977,
p. 68)

91. *The Polygamist* (*D*, Spring
1977, p. 66)

92. 1976 (*CA*, 1977, p. 233)

93. In 1912 two films were released about the Mountain Meadows Massacre. Name one.

94. What tune was "Praise God from Whom All Blessings Flow" written to?

95. In 1947, Leroy Robertson composed an oratorio based on what?

96. What important opera company in New York does Ariel Bybee McBaine sing soprano with?

97. In what language was "A Mighty Fortress" originally written?

98. What is the longest running broadcast series in the history of radio?

99. Within four, how many years did it take to construct the original Tabernacle organ, including the pipes?

100. What LDS actor played in the television series *The Family Affair?*

101. When a choir sang "The Spirit of God Like A Fire" at the Kirtland Temple dedication, where did they stand?

102. What Church attraction preserves and displays customs and crafts of the South Pacific?

103. When President David O. McKay visited Polynesia in the early 1950s, what prized art objects did the people give him?

104. Which hymn was written to commemorate the sixtieth anniversary of Queen Victoria's reign?

105. What book and chapter in the Bible is "A Poor Wayfaring Man of Grief" based on?

106. Which hymn is based on the twenty-third Psalm?

107. Which patriotic song was written while viewing the scene from atop Pikes Peak at sunrise?

108. Which song was originally called "The Tyrolian Song"?

109. Which hymn originally began with a two-measure trumpet fanfare?

110. Which hymn writer was the first president of the Deseret Hospital?

111. What government organization did the Tabernacle Choir record music for on July 11, 1944?

112. Within ten, how many years was *The Children's Friend* published?

113. "O Come All Ye Faithful" was originally a hymn of what religion?

114. Why were a group of early Mormon artists called the "20th Ward Group"?

115. What prominent Mormon woman published a romance called *John Stevens' Courtship* in 1909?

93. *Mountain Meadows Massacre*, and *The Mormon* (*D*, Spring 1977, p. 61)

94. "Old Hundred" (*SMH*, p. 226)

95. The Book of Mormon (*EN*, 7/77, p. 87)

96. The Metropolitan Opera (*BYU*, 5/78, p. 11)

97. German (*SMH*, p. 6)

98. The Tabernacle Choir broadcast (*EN*, 7/77, p. 87)

99. Twelve (*CS*, p. 23)

100. Johnnie Whitaker (*CN*, 4/14/79, p. 10)

101. At the four corners of the temple (*SMH*, p. 222)

102. The Polynesian Cultural Center (*EN*, 7/77, p. 92)

103. Baskets (*EN*, 7/77, p. 76)

104. "God of Our Fathers, Known of Old" (*SMH*, p. 91)

105. Matthew 25 (*SMH*, p. 171)

106. "The Lord Is My Shepherd" (*SMH*, p. 115)

107. "Oh Beautiful for Spacious Skies" (*SMH*, p. 129)

108. "Silent Night" (*SMH*, p. 176)

109. "God of Our Fathers, Whose Almighty Hand" (*SMH*, p. 63)

110. Eliza R. Snow (*SMH*, p. 148)

111. The United States Army (Signal Corps) (*CS*, p. 173)

112. Sixty-nine (from 1902 to 1970, inclusive) (*CA*, 1975, p. F28)

113. Catholic (*SMH*, p. viii)

114. They lived in such close proximity (*EN*, 7/77, p. 40)

115. Susa Young Gates (*BP*, p. 383)

116. The original Tabernacle Organ had seven hundred pipes. How many does the current organ have?

117. What tune was "O My Father" initially sung to?

118. What play about the life of the Prophet Joseph Smith did Ralph G. Rodgers write the script and lyrics for?

119. What position was Richard P. Condie released from in 1974, after seventeen years of service?

120. How many prominent Latter-day Saint composers have written music for "O My Father"?

121. What favorite missionary hymn was written by non-Mormons?

122. In the 1969 film *Paint Your Wagon*, what does a Mormon do in No-Name City?

123. In the 1926 movie comedy *Hands Up!* how does the hero solve his delemma of falling in love with two sisters at once?

124. In the 1911 film *A Victim of the Mormons* was produced in what European country?

125. What broadcast service did Bruce Christensen become president of in 1984?

126. Concert Pianist Wladimir Kochanski performed for what non-Mormon religious leader in 1982?

127. Which hymn was the favorite of Elder Charles A. Callis of the Council of the Twelve Apostles?

128. "Let Each Man Learn to Know Himself" was first published anonymously as a poem in what Mormon periodical?

129. B. H. Roberts wrote a love story set in what city?

130. Out of all America's newspapers, which ran the most cartoons about Mormons from 1900 to 1910?

131. Where is the Mormon Battalion Monument located?

132. Which Mormon periodical focused on arts and letters?

133. Who established the Nauvoo Dramatic Company?

134. Who won an Academy Award for a documentary in 1974?

135. What writing competition did the Relief Society begin in 1923?

136. Which song has the most versions in the 1948 edition of *Hymns* (used until 1985)?

137. "The Lord My Pasture Will Prepare" was written by which prominent member of the British Parliament?

138. Which hymn deals with the calling and commission of the Twelve Apostles?

116. More than ten thousand
     (*EN*, 7/77, p. 84)

117. "Gentle Annie," by Stephen
     Foster (*SMH*, p. 149)

118. *Joseph* (*CA*, 1980, p. 25)

119. Conductor of the Taber-
     nacle Choir (*CA*, 1975,
     p. A9)

120. Ten (*SMH*, p. 149)

121. "It May Not Be on the
     Mountain Height" (*SMH*,
     p. 91)

122. He sells his second wife (*D*,
     Spring 1977, p. 64)

123. He moves to Salt Lake City
     and marries them both (*D*,
     Spring 1977, p. 65)

124. Denmark (*D*, Spring 1977,
     p. 61)

125. Public Broadcasting Service
     (*TP*, Feb./Mar. 1985, p. 30)

126. Pope John Paul II (*TP*, 3/83,
     p. 64)

127. "O God, Our Help in Ages
     Past" (*SMH*, p. 127)

128. *Millennial Star*, in 1862
     (*SMH*, p. 103)

129. Zarahemla (*EN*, 6/81, p. 61)

130. The *Salt Lake Tribune*
     (*MGI*, p. 57)

131. San Diego, California (*EN*,
     7/77, p. 86)

132. The *Contributor* (*EN*, 7/77,
     p. 85)

133. Joseph Smith (*BP*, p. 405)

134. Kieth Merrill (*D*, Spring
     1977, p. 67)

135. Their Eliza R. Snow Poetry
     Contest (*EN*, 7/77, p. 86)

136. "O My Father" — it has four
     versions

137. Joseph Addison (*SMH*,
     p. 121)

138. "Ye Chosen Twelve, to You
     Are Given" (*SMH*, p. 219)

139. In what year was the Tabernacle Choir first commercially recorded?

140. A non-Mormon wrote the words to which hymn about the city of Zion?

141. Which hymn writer was set apart in 1880 as general president of the Relief Society?

142. What language was "Oh Come, All Ye Faithful" originally written in?

143. Which hymn writer married Brigham Young in 1849?

144. Why was the first special Tabernacle Choir concert given in the afternoon?

145. What was the earlier title of "Oh, How Lovely Was the Morning"?

146. What group received a performance award at the 1893 Chicago World's Fair?

147. Which composer has the most hymns in the 1948 edition of *Hymns* (used until 1985)?

148. When the Church refurbished an old theater in 1972, what did it rename it?

149. According to "Ere You Left Your Room This Morning," what will prayer change?

150. What is the first time of singing we have record of?

151. Who did *Billboard* magazine name the best new country music group of 1982?

152. Tabernacle organist Alexander Schreiner once doubled as a director of music for whom?

153. What did the Choral Union of Scranton, Pennsylvania, do at a singing contest in Chicago in 1893?

154. What was the Tabernacle Choir's feature number at the 1911 American Land and Irrigation Exposition in New York City?

155. When the Tabernacle Choir traveled to Europe for the first time, what menu item did their ship take pains to stock?

156. Within one hundred, how many radio stations received a copy of Val Hick's award-winning arrangment of the American national anthem?

157. Which Robert Lewis Taylor novel included Mormons?

158. What book of poetry did Emma Lou Thayne publish in 1973?

159. What Christmas television program did the Church create in 1974?

160. In a 1905 *Puck* cartoon, what did the Mormon's eight wives bring him for a surprise?

139. 1910 (*CS*, p. 196)

140. "Beautiful Zion, Built Above" (*SMH*, p. 92)

141. Eliza R. Snow (*SMH*, p. 148)

142. Latin (*SMH*, p. 134)

143. Eliza R. Snow (*SMH*, p. 147)

144. The Tabernacle had no lighting (*CS*, p. 32)

145. "Joseph Smith's First Prayer" (*SMH*, p. 140)

146. Tabernacle Choir (*EN*, 7/77, p. 87)

147. Evan Stephens (*SMH*, p. 156)

148. The Promised Valley Play-house (*EN*, 7/77, p. 86)

149. The night to day (*Hymns*, no. 31)

150. "When the morning stars sang together" (Job 38:7)

151. The Osmond Brothers (*TP*, 2/84, p. 29)

152. The Jewish congregation at Wilshire Boulevard Temple in Los Angeles (*CS*, p. 376)

153. They beat the Tabernacle Choir (*CS*, p. 68)

154. The "Irrigation Ode" (*CS*, p. 82)

155. Fresh milk, since the choir would drink no coffee or tea (*CS*, p. 109)

156. Six hundred (*CA*, 1980, p. 270)

157. *The Travels of Jaimie McPheeters* (*BP*, p. 401)

158. *Until Another Day for Butterflies*

159. *A Christmas Child* — it was broadcast over two hundred stations (*D*, Spring 1977, p. 32)

160. Their eight mothers for a month's visit (*MGI*, p. 142)

161. What contribution did Robert F. Brunner make to Walt Disney's *North Avenue Irregulars?*

162. Charles Roscoe Savage was known among the pioneers as what?

163. Within three years, in what year was *Dialogue: A Journal of Mormon Thought* founded?

164. In 1958, the magazine *Nick Nax* contrasted the American Eagle with what?

165. What sculpture did Torlief Knaphus create for Temple Square?

166. What movie did Kieth Merill make about a man's fight against the IRS?

167. Which hymn has in its refrain the words "O Galilee! Sweet Galilee!"?

168. Who painted the murals in the world room of the Manti Temple in the 1940s?

169. What position did John Henry Newman, author of "Lead, Kindly Light," hold in the Catholic Church?

170. What was the original title of "Jesus, the Very Thought of Thee"?

171. The tune to which hymn was taken from the popular song, "A Life on the Ocean Wave"?

172. What improvement was added to the Tabernacle organ in 1901?

173. Which Christmas carol was written after the author returned from a visit to the Holy Land?

174. What did *Dance Magazine* call the "ballroom pageant of the year" in 1958?

175. Which hymn was sung at the funerals of Theodore Roosevelt and Woodrow Wilson?

176. How much time did the author spend in writing the words to "Onward, Christian Soldiers"?

177. How was the original Tabernacle organ transported from California to Utah?

178. Why were Tabernacle Choir rehearsals held in the Social Hall rather than the Tabernacle in 1884?

179. Which of the many American illustrated weeklies gave the most space to the Mormons in the 1850s?

180. Who wrote the book of poetry called *The Search?*

181. What prominent scholar wrote *Since Cumorah?*

182. On what day of the year were the words to "Silent Night" written?

183. What was the full title of Parley P. Pratt's book, *The Millennium?*

184. How much time passed after the Saints arrived in the Salt Lake Valley before they organized a choir?

161. He composed the musical
score (*CN*, 5/17/80, p. 7)

162. A skilled photographer (*CA*,
1975, p. A38)

163. 1966

164. The Mormon Rooster (*MGI*,
p. 25)

165. The Handcart Family (*EN*,
7/77, p. 80)

166. *Harry's War*

167. "Each Cooing Dove"
(*Hymns*, no. 38)

168. Minerva Teichert (*EN*, 7/77,
p. 39)

169. He was a cardinal (*SMH*,
p. 120)

170. The "Rosy Hymn" (*SMH*,
p. 164)

171. "Who's on the Lord's
Side?" (*SMH*, p. 193)

172. Electric blowers (*CS*, p. 27)

173. "O Little Town of Bethlehem" (*SMH*, p. 183)

174. The Church dance festival
(*EN*, 7/77, p. 92)

175. "How Firm a Foundation"
(*SMH*, p. 78)

176. Fifteen minutes (*SMH*,
p. 133)

177. It was hauled by wagon
(*CS*, p. 21)

178. The Tabernacle was too
cold (*CS*, p. 33)

179. *Harper's Weekly* (*MGI*,
p. 24)

180. Carol Lynn Pearson (*BP*,
p. 317)

181. Hugh Nibley

182. Christmas Eve (*SMH*,
p. 176)

183. *The Millennium, and Other
Poems*

184. Two weeks (*EN*, 7/77, p. 83)

185. Within five, how many gold records have the Osmond Brothers earned?

186. Who received the George Foster Peabody Award, the Oscar of radio, in April 1944?

187. When the Tabernacle Choir recorded music in 1910, why were the ladies required to remove their hats?

188. When the Tabernacle Choir made its first tour of Europe, how many children were left behind with friends and relatives?

189. When the Tabernacle Choir prepared to take selected members to a singing contest in Chicago in 1893, how were the lucky members notified?

190. What milestone did the Tabernacle Choir pass on October 17, 1948?

191. "Krambambule," a German drinking song, is the tune for what missionary hymn?

192. What famous author did Susa Young Gates, daughter of Brigham Young, correspond with in 1886?

193. What was the original title to the Eliza R. Snow poem "O My Father"?

194. In the hymn "God Be with You" how many times in the melody line are the words "till we meet" repeated?

195. What marble statue in the capitol rotunda in Washington, D.C., did Mahonri M. Young sculpt?

196. Which General Authority wrote a novel that was later adapted to drama and performed on Broadway?

197. What major studio released the 1940 film *Brigham Young — Frontiersman?*

198. What was the first pageant put on by the Church?

199. What was the original motive power of the Tabernacle organ?

200. Merrill Jensen wrote his first motion picture music in 1976 for an important LDS film. What was it?

201. What songbook was the music for "Sing Praise to Him" taken from?

202. Who subsidized the film *One Hundred Years of Mormonism*, produced in Los Angeles in 1912–13?

203. What was the physical condition of E. E. Hewitt, author of "There's Sunshine in My Soul Today"?

204. When the Tabernacle Choir toured Europe in 1955, which hymn did it conclude every performance with?

205. What BYU motion picture has been shown extensively before Catholic and Protestant audiences?

185. Twenty-seven (*TP*, 2/84, p. 27)

186. The Mormon Tabernacle Choir (*CS*, p. 320)

187. The hats absorbed too much sound (*CS*, p. 198)

188. Six hundred (*CS*, p. 108)

189. By a notice in the *Deseret Evening News* (*CS*, p. 69)

190. It made its one-thousandth broadcast (*CS*, p. 327)

191. "The Time Is Far Spent" (*SMH*, p. 200)

192. Leo Tolstoy (*NE*, 3/71, p. 46)

193. "Invocation, or the Eternal Father and Mother" (*BP*, p. 269)

194. Twelve (*Hymns*, no. 47)

195. Brigham Young (*EN*, 7/77, p. 57)

196. B. H. Roberts (*EN*, 6/81, p. 61)

197. Twentieth Century Fox (*D*, Spring 1977, p. 66)

198. *Message of the Ages* (in 1930) (*EN*, 7/77, p. 86)

199. Four hand bellows (*CS*, p. 26)

200. *The First Vision* (*BYU*, 6/80, p. 11)

201. The Bohemian Brethren's Songbook (*SMH*, p. 174)

202. The Church (*D*, Spring 1977, p. 61)

203. She was a shut-in for years, due to a spinal malady (*SMH*, p. 193)

204. "Now the Day Is Over" (*SMH*, p. 127)

205. *Cipher in the Snow* (*EN*, 7/77, p. 87)

206. What did the film *The Rainbow Trail* (1918) emphasize in its advertising?

207. Who in Kirtland did hymn writer W. W. Phelps live with?

208. Which hymn writer has a monument erected to him in Westminster Abbey?

209. Which hymn was written by a ward leader (Joseph Townsend) who was concerned about faultfinding in his congregation?

210. According to "The First Noel," what did the star of Bethlehem do when the sun came up?

211. Which hymn speaks of humming bees, singing birds, and ringing music?

212. What is described as singing in "Firm as the Mountains Around Us"?

213. In the hymn "God Be with You," what does He keep floating over us?

214. Which hymn writer was a lawyer, a medical doctor, and a professor at Yale?

215. In 1890, the First Presidency sent John Hafen, J. B. Fairbanks, and Lorus Pratt on missions to do what?

216. The film *A Mormon Maid* (1917) showed Danite "avenging angels" in what kind of garb?

217. What organization published *The Contributor*, founded in 1879?

218. What was the original title of the tune used with "Truth Reflects upon Our Senses"?

219. What personality from *Laugh-In* appeared in *The Family . . . and Other Living Things?*

220. When the Tabernacle Choir entered a singing contest in Chicago in 1893, what prize did they win?

221. What period of Mormon history is covered in Vardis Fisher's epic novel, *Children of God?*

222. Which section of the Doctrine and Covenants provided the inspiration for a long poem Joseph Smith reportedly wrote?

223. According to the Salt Lake *Herald*, when the Tabernacle Choir traveled to Nephi, Utah, in 1884, how many people made the trip?

224. What did the composer of "Onward, Christian Soldiers," Arthur S. Sullivan, receive from Queen Victoria?

225. Who is reportedly the author of the poem that begins, "I will go, I will go, to the home of the Saints"?

226. Sharlene Wells won the talent section of what 1982 pageant?

206. A "city of sealed wives" (*D*, Spring 1977, p. 60)

207. Joseph Smith (*SMH*, p. 224)

208. Henry W. Longfellow (*SMH*, p. 230)

209. "Let Us Oft Speak Kind Words" (*SMH*, p. 75)

210. It continued to shine "both day and night" (*Hymns*, no. 39)

211. "Oh, How Lovely Was the Morning" (*Hymns*, no. 136)

212. The desert (*Hymns*, no. 42)

213. Love's banner (*Hymns*, no. 47)

214. Oliver Wendell Holmes (*SMH*, p. 280)

215. Study art in France (*EN*, 7/77, p. 40)

216. Ku Klux Klan robes (*D*, Spring 1977, p. 59)

217. The MIA (*CA*, 1975, p. F28)

218. "Life's Railway to Heaven" (*SMH*, p. 202)

219. Ruth Buzzi (*CA*, 1980, p. 17)

220. Second (*CS*, p. 68)

221. The First Vision through the Manifesto of 1890 (*EN*, 7/81, p. 57)

222. D&C 76 (*BP*, p. 258)

223. 173½ (*CS*, p. 60)

224. Knighthood (*SMH*, p. 134)

225. Joseph Smith (*BP*, p. 258)

226. America's Junior Miss (*CA*, 1983, p. 249)

227. What hymn contains the words "the day is past and gone"?

228. Which song was written to commemorate the one hundreth anniversary of the American Declaration of Independence?

229. Give the last name of the brothers who wrote *The Bishop's Horse Race.*

230. What famed Mormon pianist has been knighted?

231. Which hymn was originally written as a rally song against the Roman Catholic Church?

232. What were Universal Scientific societies of nineteenth-century Utah designed to do?

233. What was poet Ina Coolbrith's relationship to Joseph Smith?

234. Who sculpted the Brigham Young Memorial on Salt Lake City's Main Street?

235. How many verses are in the hymn "A Mighty Fortress"?

236. How many songs have three or more versions in the 1948 edition of *Hymns* (used until 1985)?

237. How many stanzas were originally included in "Now the Day Is Over"?

238. What were Ward Institutes of nineteenth-century Utah designed to do?

239. Where was the original Tabernacle organ first constructed?

240. Which hymn was written after the author, Philip Bliss, had a close call at sea on a foggy night?

241. What did the Tabernacle Choir help reenact over the air on April 6, 1943?

242. In the hymn "Behold! A Royal Army," what is the army carrying?

243. What famous classical composer wrote the music to "Hark! The Herald Angels Sing"?

244. Which hymn was written by the man who succeeded William Wordsworth as poet laureate of England?

245. Within two, how many stanzas did "Hark! The Herald Angels Sing" originally have?

246. What hymn was authored by a man who served more than one prison term because of his political beliefs?

247. What scripture is the hymn "I Saw a Mighty Angel Fly" based on?

248. Naomi Ward Randall is best known for what song?

249. How many verses are in "Come, Follow Me"?

250. In 1897, *Tip Top Weekly* showed what imaginary Mormon response to bicycles?

227. "Abide with Me; 'Tis Eventide" (*Hymns*, no. 2)

228. "God of Our Fathers, Whose Almighty Hand" (*SMH*, p. 63)

229. Yorgason (Blaine and Brenton)

230. Wladimir Kochanski (*TP*, 3/83, p. 63)

231. "A Mighty Fortress" (*SMH*, p. 6)

232. Promote cultural appreciation (*EN*, 7/77, p. 85)

233. Niece (*BP*, p. 276)

234. Cyrus E. Dallin (*EN*, 7/77, p. 85)

235. One (*Hymns*, no. 3)

236. Twelve

237. Eight (*SMH*, p. 127)

238. Promote cultural appreciation (*EN*, 7/77, p. 85)

239. Australia (*CS*, p. 21)

240. "Brightly Beams Our Father's Mercy" (*SMH*, p. 288)

241. The dedication of the Salt Lake Temple, which occurred exactly fifty years earlier (*CS*, p. 170)

242. "Banner, sword, and shield" (*Hymns*, no. 7)

243. Felix Mendelssohn (*SMH*, p. 67)

244. "Ring Out, Wild Bells," by Alfred, Lord Tennyson (*SMH*, p. 274)

245. Ten (*SMH*, p. 67)

246. "A Poor Wayfaring Man of Grief," by Montgomery (*SMH*, p. 171)

247. Revelation 14:6−7 (*SMH*, p. 256)

248. "I Am a Child of God" (*BP*, p. 328)

249. Six (*Hymns*, no. 14)

250. They rejected them as inventions of the devil (*MGI*, p. 58)

251. In a 1906 *Puck* cartoon, what did "Cupid in Utah" use for a weapon?

252. Wladimir Kochanski has been acclaimed by many as many as the greatest pianist since whom?

253. What pageant did the Church put on in commemoration of its one-hundredth anniversary?

254. Where were the first auditions for the Tabernacle Choir held?

255. When a public adress system was installed in the Tabernacle to help the choir hear the organ better, where was the microphone placed?

256. On the average, how often does the Tabernacle Choir add a new hymn to its repertoire?

257. What Mormon publication was the second women's magazine in the United States?

258. What popular ballad was formerly the tune used with "There Is a Green Hill Far Away"?

259. What Church member starred in *Bonanza?*

260. Which Christmas hymn was written by Nahum Tate, the poet laureate to the king of England?

261. Which hymn tune was adapted from "The Old Oaken Bucket"?

262. Which General Authority wrote a lengthy epic poem entitled *Elias, An Epic of the Ages?*

263. What prominent business-man and author was a solist for the Tabernacle Choir in 1954?

264. What percentage of the hymns in the Church's first hymnbook continued into the 1948 edition (which was used until 1985)?

265. The first Church dance festival was held at what resort in 1928?

266. Where did most of the wood come from that was used in the original Tabernacle organ?

267. In 1915, the First Presidency encouraged singing in the home in conjunction with what?

268. What were philomathian societies of nineteenth-century Utah designed to do?

269. What Church attraction has received rave reviews from Broadway's publication, *Variety?*

270. What magnificent 3-D film did the Tabernacle Choir appear in during the early 1950s?

271. What tune was "O Ye Mountains High" written to?

251. A machine gun (*MGI*, p. 140)

252. Paderewski (*TP*, 3/83, p. 63)

253. *The Message of the Ages*

254. In the home of the conductor (*CS*, p. 10)

255. In the organ (*CS*, p. 53)

256. Once a week (*CS*, p. 36)

257. *Women's Exponent*

258. "Drink to Me Only with Thine Eyes" (*SMH*, p. 214)

259. Dan Blocker

260. "While Shepherds Watched Their Flocks by Night" (*SMH*, p. 233)

261. "Do What Is Right" (*SMH*, p. 36)

262. Orson F. Whitney (*BP*, p. 203)

263. Howard Ruff (*TP*, Con. 1982, p. 18)

264. About one-third (*SMH*, p. xxii)

265. Saltair, on the Great Salt Lake (*EN*, 7/77, p. 92)

266. The canyons of Utah (*CS*, p. 22)

267. The Home Evening Program (*EN*, 7/77, p. 85)

268. Promote cultural appreciation (*EN*, 7/77, p. 85)

269. The Polynesian Cultural Center (*EN*, 7/77, p. 92)

270. *This Is Cinerama* (*CS*, p. 191)

271. The Scotch ditty "O Minnie, O Minnie, Come o'er the Lea" (*SMH*, p. 159)

272. In the 1860s, Utah Territory had forty musical bands. How many did it have by 1875?

273. What movie did Doty-Dayton Productions make about a boy and his dogs?

274. Which hymn did Arthur S. Sullivan, of Gilbert and Sullivan fame, compose the music for?

275. For what occasion was "We Love Thy House, O God" written?

276. Name one of the two sections of the Doctrine and Covenants that command us to seek wisdom out of the best books?

277. The music for "O God, the Eternal Father" was taken from a song by which prominent composer?

278. When the Tabernacle Choir made a tour of the East in 1911, which city in New York refused to let them appear because of opposition to the Church?

279. Within five hundred, how many hymns is religious reformer Charles Wesley credited with writing?

280. What important reformer wrote "A Mighty Fortress"?

281. Within five, how many poems by Eliza R. Snow are in the 1948 *Hymns* (the edition used until 1985)?

282. What actor played Orrin Porter Rockwell in the 1940 movie *Brigham Young — Frontiersman?*

283. Where was Parley P. Pratt's "The Morning Breaks; the Shadows Flee" first published?

284. What was the primary type of wood used for the pipes of the original Tabernacle organ?

285. In 1974, Robert Bowden became director of what Mormon musical group?

286. What music conservatory was sponsored by the Church?

287. Which hymn contains the words "Our time as a stream"?

288. How large was the audience at the 1976 Tabernacle Choir Washington Monument performance?

289. What was installed in 1895 to pump the Tabernacle organ?

290. Which hymn won a contest to become the MIA theme song in 1930?

291. Which hymn uses the tune from "The Officer's Funeral March"?

292. What Apostle wrote the humorous "A Dialogue Between Joseph Smith and the Devil"?

272. Eighty (*EN*, 7/77, p. 84)

273. *Where the Red Fern Grows* (*D*, Spring 1977, p. 67)

274. "Onward, Christian Soldiers" (*SMH*, p. 134)

275. The dedication of a Protestant chapel in Nova Scotia (*SMH*, p. 215)

276. Sections 88 and 109 (D&C 88:118, 109:7)

277. Felix Mendelssohn (*SMH*, p. 129)

278. Buffalo, New York (*CS*, p. 79)

279. 6,500 (*SMH*, p. viii)

280. Martin Luther (*SMH*, p. 6)

281. Twenty-two (*SMH*, p. 82)

282. John Carradine (*D*, Spring 1977, p. 64)

283. *Millennial Star* (1840) (*SMH*, p. 263)

284. Yellow pine (*CS*, p. 23)

285. Mormon Youth Symphony and Chorus (*CA*, 1975, p. A56)

286. The McCune School of Music and Art (*CS*, p. 373)

287. "Come, Let Us Anew" (*Hymns*, no. 17)

288. One million (another million watched on television) (*EN*, 7/77, p. 92)

289. A hydraulic system (*CS*, p. 26)

290. "Firm as the Mountains Around Us" (*SMH*, p. 49)

291. "We Thank Thee, O God, for a Prophet" (*SMH*, p. 209)

292. Parley P. Pratt (*BP*, p. 333)

293. What major musical event occurred in Utah in 1875?

294. "Up, Awake, Ye Defenders of Zion" was written to what tune?

295. Name one of the two distant cousins to President Kimball who were prominent nineteenth-century poets.

296. Which Utah temple did John Hafen paint murals in?

297. What is the name of the series of public service "spot" announcements the Church produces?

298. Which pioneer home has been named by one group of architects as one of the thirty "great houses of America"?

299. "Praise to the Man" is based on a folk song from what country?

300. What sculpture on Temple Square did Cyrus E. Dallin create?

Simpler Questions for Use as Needed

301. What is the name of the song that says in the chorus, "For some must push and some must pull"?

302. What is the name of the Church choir that sings on Temple Square every week?

303. How does the song end that begins, "I love Mother; she loves me."

304. Which entertainer helped the Osmonds early in their career — Andy Williams, Elvis Presley, or John Denver?

305. "For health and strength and_____ _____we praise thy name."

306. How old was Marie Osmond when she first performed on stage — four, six, eight, or ten?

307. "If you chance to meet a frown, do not let it stay. Quickly turn it upside down and_____that frown away."

308. In the song "Our Primary Colors," does yellow stand for courage, service, or purity?

309. In the song "My Heavenly Father Loves Me," what did he give me my eyes "that I might see"?

310. True or false: Merlin Olsen was an actor on *Little House on the Prairie.*

311. True or false: The Osmonds have performed for President Ronald Reagan.

312. "Our prophet has some words for you, and these are the words:_____ _____.''

293. *The Messiah* was first performed in Utah (*SMH*, p. 266)

294. "The Red, White, and Blue," also known as "Columbia, the Gem of the Ocean" (*SMH*, p. 45)

295. William Cullen Bryant, Henry Wadsworth Longfellow (*NS*, p. 40)

296. Salt Lake Temple (*EN*, 7/77, p. 57)

297. "Homefront" (*D*, Spring 1977, p. 32)

298. Brigham Young's Beehive House (*EN*, 7/77, p. 84)

299. Scotland (*SMH*, p. 164)

300. The Angel Moroni (*EN*, 7/77, p. 85)

301. "The Handcart Song" (*BP*, p. 255)

302. Mormon Tabernacle Choir

303. "We are a happy family" (*SWM*, p. D-1)

304. Andy Williams

305. "Daily food" (*SWM*, p. B-33)

306. Six (*TP*, June/July 1982, p. 18)

307. "Smile" (*SWM*, p. D-5)

308. Service (*SWM*, p. B-62)

309. "The color of butterfly wings" (*SWM*, p. B-59)

310. True

311. True

312. "Be true" (*SWM*, p. B-37)

313. Are Arnold Friberg's paintings found in some copies of the Bible, Book of Mormon, Doctrine and Covenants, or Pearl of Great Price?

314. In the song "I'm so glad when Daddy comes home," what do you pat?

315. "Jesus wants me for a sunbeam, to_____for him each day."

316. Alan Cassidy helped write the stories about a television superhero. Which show did he write for?

317. Name the Glen Larson television show that starred Lee Majors as a bionic man.

318. "Teach me to walk in the light of his_____."

319. Jay North joined the Church in 1978. What impish boy did he play on television many years earlier?

320. Which Disney character did Christian Jacobs play on a record album — Pinocchio, Peter Pan, Bambi, or Mr. Toad?

321. "Dare to do_____! dare to be_____!"

322. In the song, where did "the golden plates lay hidden"?

323. Did Kieth Merrill win an Academy Award for a movie about dolphins, baseball, or rodeo cowboys?

324. In the song, what do "the chapel doors seem to say"?

325. "I will try to be reverent when I'm in his_____."

326. Which member of the Osmond family starred in the movie *The Great Brain* — Donny, Merrill, Jimmy, or Marie?

327. A Primary song has the words "Your happy smiling face is such a joy to look at." How does that song begin?

328. Sherry Hill won an Idaho contest playing what musical instrument — piano, flute, or fiddle?

329. True or false: Church member Glen Larson worked on the TV show called *Battlestar Galactica.*

330. In the song "Thanks to Our Father," what are the first four things we thank him for?

331. What television show about a talking car was produced by Glen Larson?

332. "When we're helping we're happy, and we_____as we go."

333. In the song "Dare to Do Right," who will "hasten the story to tell" if we make right choices?

334. In the Primary song, what are the birds "in the leafy treetops" singing?

335. True or false: Marie Osmond has been on the *Tonight Show.*

313. Book of Mormon

314. "His cheeks" (*SWM*, p. D-19)

315. "Shine" (*SWM*, p. B-67)

316. *The Incredible Hulk* (*BYU*, 6/80, p. 10)

317. *Six Million Dollar Man*

318. "Love" (*SWM*, p. B-45)

319. Dennis the Menace (*CN*, 9/23/78, p. 4)

320. Bambi (*TP*, 3/83, p. 65)

321. "Dare to do *right*! dare to be *true*!" (*SWM*, p. B-81)

322. "Deep in a mountain side" (*SWM*, p. B-57)

323. Rodeo cowboys

324. "Sh, be still" (*SWM*, p. B-56)

325. "House" (*SWM*, p. A-1)

326. Jimmy (*CA*, 1979, p. 252)

327. "Mother dear, I love you so" (*SWM*, p. D-3)

328. Fiddle

329. True

330. "Eyes and ears and hands and feet" (*SWM*, p. A-3)

331. *Knight Rider*

332. "Sing" (*SWM*, p. D-5)

333. Angels (*SWM*, p. B-81)

334. "Good morning" (*SWM*, p. G-5)

335. True

336. In the Primary song, what will happen "when your heart is filled with love"?

337. "When my mother calls me, quickly_____ _____."

338. What statue did Avard Fairbanks create for the outside of the Salt Lake Temple?

339. What did pioneer children do "as they walked and walked and walked and walked"?

340. "If with all your_____ye truly seek me."

341. True or false: Merlin Olsen starred in the TV show *Father Murphy*.

342. Name the Glen Larson television show that starred Lee Majors as a stunt man.

343. "A special gift is_____."

344. How old was Joseph Daynes when Brigham Young said he would become Tabernacle organist—nine, eleven, thirteen, or fifteen?

345. "I often go walking in meadows of_____."

346. "Jesus once was a_____ _____."

347. "Book of Mormon stories that my teacher tells to me, are about the_____in ancient history."

348. True or false: A Church member was one of the stars of the TV show *Bonanza*.

349. In the song, when do "I always have a happy feeling"?

350. Johnnie Whitaker starred in the movie *Tom Sawyer*. Later he stopped making movies so he could do something for the Church. What was it?

336. "Others will love you" (*SWM*, p. B-51)

337. "I'll obey" (*SWM*, p. B-36)

338. The statue of the Angel Moroni (*CN*, 5/24/80, p. 14)

339. They sang (*SWM*, p. E-1)

340. "Hearts" (*SWM*, p. B-72)

341. True

342. *The Fall Guy*

343. "Kindness" (*SWM*, p. B-1)

344. Eleven (*CS*, p. 366)

345. "Clover" (*SWM*, p. D-15)

346. "Little child" (*SWM*, p. B-66)

347. "Lamanites" (*SWM*, B-87)

348. True (Dan Blocker, as Hoss Cartwright)

349. "When I go to church" (*SWM*, p. B-52)

350. He went on a mission (*CN*, · 4/14/79, p. 10)